TINY TRAINS

A Guide to Britain's Miniature Railways 2019-2020

EDITOR
Steve Askew

Thirteenth Edition

RAILWAY LOCATOR MAP

The numbers shown on this map relate to the page numbers for each railway.
Pages 5-6 contain an alphabetical listing of the railways featured in this guide.
Please note that the markers on this map show the approximate location only.

ACKNOWLEDGEMENTS

We were greatly impressed by the friendly and cooperative manner of the staff and helpers of the railways and societies which we selected to appear in this book, and wish to thank them all for the help they have given. In addition we wish to thank Bob Budd (cover design), Michael Robinson (page layouts) and Jonathan James (photographs) for their help.

Although we believe that the information contained in this guide is accurate at the time of going to press, we, and the Railways and Societies itemised, are unable to accept liability for any loss, damage, distress or injury suffered as a result of any inaccuracies. Furthermore, we and the Societies are unable to guarantee operating and opening times which may always be subject to cancellation without notice. For the purposes of this guide we classify railways with gauges of 7¼ inches or less as 'miniature'.

Steve Askew

EDITOR

COVER PHOTOGRAPH

The cover photograph was taken by Jonathan James on 19th May 2018 at the South Devon Miniature Railway and shows the 0-4-0 petrol locomotive D2203 'Phoenix' in operation.

British Library Cataloguing in Publication Data
A catalogue record for this book is available from the British Library

ISBN-13: 978-1-86223-400-0

Copyright © 2019, SOCCER BOOKS LIMITED. (01472 696226)
72 St. Peter's Avenue, Cleethorpes, N.E. Lincolnshire, DN35 8HU, England

Printed in the UK by TJ International Ltd.

CONTENTS

Railway Locator Map (North) 2
Railway Locator Map (South) 3
Acknowledgements 4
Contents 5-6
Abbeydale Miniature Railway 7
Amnerfield Miniature Railway 8
Ashmanhaugh Light Railway 9
Ashton Court Estate Miniature Railway 10
Avonvale Model Engineering Society 11
Barnards Miniature Railway 12
Barton House Railway 13
Bath & West Railway 14
Beer Heights Light Railway 15
Bekonscot Light Railway 16
Bentley Miniature Railway 17
Bridgend & District Model Engineering Society 18
Brighouse & Halifax Model Engineers 19
Bromsgrove Society of Model Engineers 20
Brookside Miniature Railway 21
Broomy Hill Railway 22
Burnley & Pendle Miniature Railway Society (Thompson Park Railway) 23
Cambridge & District Model Engineering Society 24
Canterbury & District Model Engineering Society 25
Canvey Miniature Railway 26
Cardiff Model Engineering Society 27
Chelmsford Society of Model Engineers 28
Chingford & District Model Engineering Club 29
Coate Water Park Miniature Railway 30
Conwy Valley Railway Museum 31
Crowborough Miniature Railway 32
Cutteslowe Park Miniature Railway 33
Devon Railway Centre 34
Dragon Miniature Railway 35
Eastbourne Miniature Steam Railway 36
East Herts Miniature Railway 37
Evergreens Miniature Railway 38
Frimley Lodge Miniature Railway 39
Golding Spring Miniature Railway 40
Great Cockcrow Railway 41
Grimsby & Cleethorpes Model Engineering Society 42
Grosvenor Park Miniature Railway 43
Halton Miniature Railway 44
Hilcote Valley Railway 45
Hollycombe – Steam in the Country 46
Hull & District Society of Model and Experimental Engineers 47
Ickenham Miniature Railway 48

Ilford & West Essex Model Railway Club 49
Kinver & West Midlands Society of Model Engineers 50
Langford & Beeleigh Railway 51
Leicester Society of Model Engineers 52
Littledown Miniature Railway 53
Little Hay Miniature Railway 54
Little Western Railway 55
Llwyfan Cerrig Miniature Railway 56
Moors Valley Railway 57
National Railway Museum 58
Ness Islands Railway 59
North Scarle Miniature Railway 60
Northampton Society of Model Engineers 61
Norwich & District Society of Model Engineers 62
Picnic Field Railway 63
Pinewood Miniature Railway 64
Plymouth Miniature Steam 65
Poplar Miniature Railway 66
Porterswick Junction Light Railway 67
Porthmadog Woodland Railway 68
Pugneys Light Railway 69
Rainsbrook Valley Railway 70
Reading Society of Model Engineers 71
Roxbourne Park Miniature Railway 72
Royds Park Miniature Railway 73
Ryedale Society of Model Engineers 74
Scottish Model Engineering Trust 75
Stansted Park Light Railway 76
Stoke Park Railway 77
Strand Miniature Railway 78
Strathaven Miniature Railway 79
Strawberry Line Miniature Railway 80
Summerfields Miniature Railway 81
Surrey Society of Model Engineers 82
Swanley New Barn Railway 83
Thames Ditton Miniature Railway 84
Thornes Park Miniature Railway 85
Tonbridge Model Engineering Society 86
Urmston Miniature Railway 87
Vogrie Park Miniature Railway 88
Welling & District Model Engineering Society 89
West Huntspill Model Engineering Society 90
Weston Park Railway 91
Willen Lake Miniature Railway 92
Woking Miniature Railway 93
Wolds Way Lavender 94
Wolverhampton & District Model Engineers Society 95
Woodseaves Railway 96

ABBEYDALE MINIATURE RAILWAY

Address: Abbeydale Road South, Sheffield S17 3LB **Telephone N°**: None **Year Formed**: 1900 (Operating in the current location since 1978) **Location of Line**: Abbeydale Road South **Length of Line**: 1,000 yards ground-level, 200 yards elevated	**N° of Steam Locos**: 10+ **N° of Other Locos**: 8+ **N° of Members**: Approximately 135 **Approx N° of Visitors P.A.**: 18,000+ **Gauges**: 2½ inches, 3½ inches, 5 inches and 7¼ inches **Web**: www.sheffieldmodelengineers.com **E-mail**: micksavage@talktalk.net

GENERAL INFORMATION

Nearest Mainline Station: Dore & Totley (200 yards)
Nearest Bus Station: Sheffield (4½ miles). The 97, 98 and 218 bus services stop outside the railway.
Car Parking: Limited spaces available on site
Coach Parking: Street parking only
Souvenir Shop(s): Yes
Food & Drinks: Available

SPECIAL INFORMATION

The Railway is operated by the Sheffield and District Society of Model and Experimental Engineers. The railway itself is located very close to the historical Abbeydale Industrial Hamlet, a unique 18th Century industrial works and one of the largest water-powered sites on the River Sheaf.

OPERATING INFORMATION

Opening Times: 2019 dates: 24th March, 14th & 28th April; 12th May; 2nd, 16th, 29th & 30th June; 14th & 28th July; 11th August; 1st, 15th & 29th September. Also open during dates in December for Santa Specials. Check the web site for details. Usually open 1.00pm to 5.00pm.
Steam Working: Most operating days.
Prices: £1.50 per ride

Detailed Directions by Car:
From the South: Exit the M1 at Junction 29 and take the A617 to Chesterfield. Then take the A61 towards Sheffield until you reach the Meadowhead roundabout on the outskirts of Sheffield. Take the first exit signposted A621 to Bakewell, then bear right. Follow signs to Bakewell & Abbeydale Industrial Hamlet. The railway entrance is on the right 200 yards past the Hamlet; From the North and East: Exit the M1 at Junction 33 and take the A630 towards Sheffield. After about 4 miles join the A6102 (Prince of Wales Road). Follow the A6102 (outer ring road) until you reach the Meadowhead roundabout (A61). Take the 2nd exit signposted A621 to Bakewell, then as above; From the West: Take the A621 to Sheffield. Pass through Totley then look out for Dore and Totley Station on your right. The railway entrance is on the left after about 150 yards.

AMNERFIELD MINIATURE RAILWAY

Address: Amners Farm, Burghfield, Berkshire   RG30 3UE
Telephone Nº: (0118) 983-3437 or 07836 714463
Year Formed: 1995
Location of Line: Amners Farm
Length of Line: ¾ mile

Nº of Steam Locos: 4
Nº of Other Locos: 5
Nº of Members: 13
Approx Nº of Visitors P.A.: 10,000
Gauge: 5 inches and 7¼ inches
Web site: www.amnersfarm.co.uk

GENERAL INFORMATION

Nearest Mainline Station: Theale (2 miles)
Nearest Bus Station: Reading
Car Parking: Free parking available on site
Coach Parking: None
Souvenir Shop(s): None
Food & Drinks: Available

SPECIAL INFORMATION

Amners Farm is a working farm which dates back to the 12th Century. Trains only run on lambing days when there is also an entrance fee charged. Other activities available include a Pets' Corner, pony rides, childrens straw play barn plus many more.

OPERATING INFORMATION

Opening Times: 2019 dates: 27th & 28th April; 4th, 5th & 6th May; Other operating dates may be announced so please check the web site for further details of these.
Trains run from 11.00am to 5.00pm
Steam Working: Every operating day.
Prices: Adults £8.50
          Children £5.00
          Family £25.00 (2 adults + 2 children)
Tickets are cheaper if purchased in advance of the visit.
Note: Train rides are an additional charge of £1.50

Detailed Directions by Car:
From All Parts: Exit the M4 at Junction 12 and take the A4 towards Reading. After approximately 2 miles turn right at the traffic lights into Burghfield Road. Continue along this road passing over the motorway then take the first turning on the left into Amners Farm Road. After approximately ½ mile turn right into Amners Farm.

ASHMANHAUGH LIGHT RAILWAY

Address: East View Farm, Stone Lane, Ashmanhaugh, Norwich NR12 8YW **Telephone Nº:** (01603) 404263 **Year Formed:** 2002 **Location of Line:** Near Wroxham Barns **Length of Line:** 900 yards	**Nº of Steam Locos:** 4 **Nº of Other Locos:** 8 **Approx Nº of Visitors P.A.:** 2,500 **Gauge:** 7¼ inches **Web site:** www.ashmanhaughlightrailway.co.uk

GENERAL INFORMATION

Nearest Mainline Station: Wroxham & Hoveton (1½ miles)
Nearest Bus Station: Norwich (10 miles)
Car Parking: Free parking is available on site
Coach Parking: None
Souvenir Shop(s): None
Food & Drinks: Light refreshments available

SPECIAL INFORMATION

Close to the Bure Valley Line and the Norwich to Sheringham Line, this is a railway operated by enthusiasts set in the beautiful North Norfolk countryside on a delightful 10 acre landscaped site.

OPERATING INFORMATION

Opening Times: 2019 dates: The first Sunday in the month from 5th May to 6th October inclusive, weather permitting.
Trains run from 2.00pm to 5.00pm.
Steam Working: Most operating days.
Prices: Single Ride tickets £2.00
　　　　　Day Rover tickets £4.00
Note: Dogs are not allowed on the site.

Detailed Directions by Car:
From All Parts: Ashmanhaugh is situated just off the A1151 Wroxham to Stalham road. The railway is close to the Wroxham Barns Centre and is signposted from the road on open days.

ASHTON COURT ESTATE MINIATURE RAILWAY

Address: Ashton Court Estate, Long Ashton, North Somerset   BS8 3PX
Telephone Nº: (0117) 946-7110
Year Formed: Opened 1973
Location of Line: Ashton Court Estate
Length of Line: Two tracks, each approximately a third of a mile in length

Nº of Steam Locos: 3
Nº of Other Locos: 4
Nº of Members: 250
Approx Nº of Visitors P.A.: 30,000
Gauge: 3½ inches, 5 inches & 7¼ inches
Website: www.bristolmodelengineers.co.uk

GENERAL INFORMATION

Nearest Mainline Station: Bristol Temple Meads (Approximately 5 miles)
Nearest Bus Station: Bristol (4 miles)
Car Parking: Pay and Display adjacent to the site
Coach Parking: Available by prior arrangement
Souvenir Shop(s): None
Food & Drinks: None

SPECIAL INFORMATION

The Railway is owned and operated by the Bristol Society of Model & Experimental Engineers which was founded in 1909.

OPERATING INFORMATION

Opening Times: 2019 dates: 31st March; 7th, 21st & 22nd April; 5th, 6th, 19th, 26th & 27th May; 9th, 16th & 30th June; 14th & 21st July; 4th, 18th, 25th & 26th August; 8th & 22nd September; 6th, 13th & 27th October and Santa Specials on 1st December (pre-booking required). On operating days, trains run from 12.00pm to 5.00pm, weather permitting.
Steam Working: All operating days.
Prices: £1.50p per ride per person. Also 5 tickets available for £6.50
Note: Tickets for the very popular Santa Specials are pre-bookable from 4th August.

Detailed Directions by Car:
Exit the M5 at junction 19 and take the A369 towards Bristol. After approximately 6 miles, just past the B3129 traffic lights is Ashton Court Estate. However, there is no right turn from this direction. Instead, take the side road on the left (North Road), turn right into Bridge Road and continue straight across the A369 at the traffic lights into the Clifton Lodge Entrance. Take the first right then the first right again before the golf kiosk car park.

AVONVALE MODEL ENGINEERING SOCIETY

Address: Hillers, Heath Farm, Alcester
Warwickshire   B49 5PD
Phone Nº: (01527) 543350
Year Formed: 2001
Location of Line: Hillers, Dunnington
Length of Line: A third of a mile

Nº of Steam Locos: 16
Nº of Other Locos: 12
Nº of Members: Approximately 40
Approx Nº of Visitors P.A.: 3,000
Gauge: 5 inches and 7¼ inches
Web site: www.avonvale.me.uk

GENERAL INFORMATION

Nearest Mainline Station: Evesham (11 miles)
Nearest Bus Station: Stratford-upon-Avon (13 miles)
Car Parking: Free parking available on site
Coach Parking: None
Souvenir Shop(s): None
Food & Drinks: Available

SPECIAL INFORMATION

The Engines are all privately owned and run as required. The railway is located at Hillers where other attractions include a Café, a Farm Shop and a Display Garden.

OPERATING INFORMATION

Opening Times: 2019 dates: 6th, 7th, 20th & 21st April; 4th, 5th, 25th & 26th May; 8th, 9th, 22nd & 23rd June; 6th, 7th, 20th & 21st July; 3rd, 4th, 24th & 25th August; 7th, 8th, 21st, 22nd & 28th September; 5th, 6th, 19th & 20th October. Also a special Halloween event on 30th & 31st October. Trains run from 11.00am to 4.00pm and from 3.00pm to 8.00pm on Halloween event days.
Steam Working: Where possible at least two steam locos run on each operating day.
Prices: £1.00 per ride per person on normal days
8 tickets cost £7.00
£1.20 per ride on Halloween events

Detailed Directions by Car:
From the North: Take the A435 or A46 to Alcester then follow the B4088 to Dunnington. Once in Dunnington, turn right at the crossroad and Hillers is on the right hand side with the railway visible from the road; From the South: Take the Evesham bypass then follow the B4088 to Dunnington.

BARNARDS MINIATURE RAILWAY

Address: Barnards Farm, Brentwood Road, West Horndon CM13 3LX
Telephone Nº: (01277) 811262
Year Formed: 2010
Location: Off the A128 between Basildon & Hornchurch
Length of Line: Almost 1 mile

Nº of Steam Locos: 9
Nº of Other Locos: 6
Approx Nº of Visitors P.A.: 3,000
Gauge: 7¼ inches
Web: www.barnardsminiaturerailway.eu
E-mail: bmr@barnardsminiaturerailway.eu

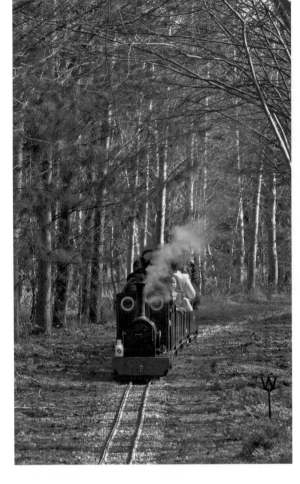

GENERAL INFORMATION

Nearest Mainline Station: West Horndon (1½ miles)
Car Parking: Available on site
Coach Parking: Available on site
Souvenir Shop(s): None
Food & Drinks: Available on site

SPECIAL INFORMATION

The Railway is located at Barnards Farm and runs through 17 hectares of gardens which range from landscaped walks through young woodland to the precise detail of the Japanese garden. A significant collection of sculpture by artists of many nationalities is also spread throughout the gardens. The gardens are open to the public on certain days during the year and visitors to the railway will need to pay an additional entrance fee on these days. Please check www.barnardsfarm.eu for further information.

OPERATING INFO

Opening Times: Due to significant works to the track during 2019, the first operating day will be on 30th June. Please check the web site for subsequent running days. The gardens are generally open from 11.00am to 4.30pm though they only open on afternoons on other dates. Please contact Barnards Farm for details.
Steam Working: Please contact the railway for further information.
Prices: Adult Return £6.00
 Child Return £5.00
 (Under-3s ride free)
 Adult All Day Travel Ticket £10.00
 Child All Day Travel Ticket £8.00
Note: Advance bookings are required for the Santa Specials which operate during December. Group visits can often be arranged by appointment.

Detailed Directions by Car:
From the West: Exit the M25 at Junction 29 and head eastward on the A127. After approximately 6½ miles exit onto the A128 and follow the road towards Tilbury. Turn right into the Barnard Farm car park shortly after passing under the railway line; From the East: Follow the A127 westward from Basildon and exit onto the A128 towards Tilbury. Then as above.

BARTON HOUSE RAILWAY

Address: Hartwell Road, The Avenue, Wroxham NR12 8TL **Telephone Nº**: (01603) 782008 **Year Formed**: 1963 **Location of Line**: Wroxham, Norfolk **Length of Line**: 167 yards	**Nº of Steam Locos**: 4 **Nº of Other Locos**: 4 **Approx Nº of Visitors P.A.**: 1,250 **Gauge**: 3½ inches and 7¼ inches **Web site**: www.bartonhouserailway.org.uk **Email**: enquiries@bartonhouserailway.org.uk

GENERAL INFO

Nearest Mainline Station: Hoveton and Wroxham (1 mile)
Nearest Bus Station: Wroxham (1 mile)
Car Parking: Limited parking available on site
Coach Parking: None
Souvenir Shop(s): Yes
Food & Drinks: Available

SPECIAL INFO

The original Honing East signalbox was rebuilt at Wroxham to form the basis for the Barton House Railway which is run entirely by volunteers. On open days, a boat service operates from Wroxham Bridge to take passengers to the railway.

OPERATING INFO

Opening Times: The 3rd Sunday each month from April until October and also on Easter Monday. Trains run from 2.30pm to 5.30pm. Also open on the 3rd Saturday in September from 7.00pm to 10.00pm.
Steam Working: Most operating days.
Prices: Adults £3.00
Children £1.50
Note: On open days, access to the railway is also available via an electric launch service running from Wroxham Bridge. Prices of this service are shown above.

Detailed Directions by Car:
From the South and West: Take the A1151 from Norwich to Wroxham then follow the road over the railway bridge. Take the 3rd turning on the right into 'The Avenue', first left into Staitheway Road then right into Hartwell Road. The railway is at the end of the road; From the North: Take the A149 to the A1151 to Wroxham, turn left into 'The Avenue', then as above.

BATH & WEST RAILWAY

Address: The Royal Bath and West Showground, Shepton Mallet BA4 6QN	**No of Members:** Approximately 100
Year Formed: 2001	**Annual Membership Fee:** £28.00
Length of Line: ½ mile	**Approx No of Visitors P.A.:** 11,000
No of Steam Locos: 11	**Gauge:** 5 inches and 7¼ inches
No of Other Locos: 3	**Web site:** www.essmee.org.uk
	Contact E-mail: chair@essmee.org.uk

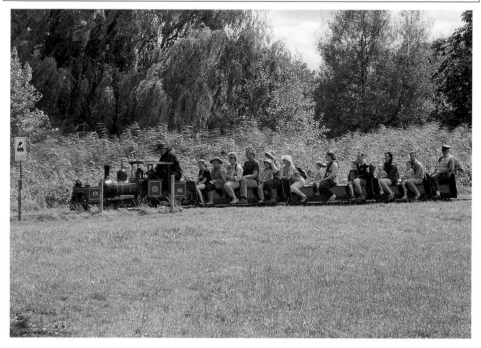

GENERAL INFORMATION

Nearest Mainline Station: Castle Cary (4 miles)
Nearest Bus Station: Shepton Mallet
Car Parking: Free parking available on site
Coach Parking: Available
Food & Drinks: Available during shows

SPECIAL INFORMATION

The Bath & West Railway is operated by members of the East Somerset Society of Model and Experimental Engineers Ltd.

OPERATING INFORMATION

Opening Times: The railway is situated on The Royal Bath & West Showground, Shepton Mallet. Our operating days, as well as our ability to entertain visitors with their locos, are therefore governed by which particular shows are using the showground. The railway operates on the four days of the Royal Bath & West Show from 29th May to 1st June 2019. Agreements between the Society and other shows may mean that the railway also operates on other dates during 2019. Please check the Society's web site for public running dates in 2019 before visiting. The Society has two open weekends planned for 2019, 27th & 28th April and 5th & 6th October when members of the public and other Engineering Societies are invited to visit with their locos and traction engines. Contact details to arrange this can be found on the web site.
Steam Working: All public operating days.
Prices: £2.00 per ride. Also 6 rides for £10.00 or 10 rides for £15.00
Note: An entrance fee is charged by the show organisers for their events.

Detailed Directions by Car:
From All Parts: The Royal Bath and West Showground is situated approximately 2 miles south of Shepton Mallet just off the A371 road to Castle Cary.

BEER HEIGHTS LIGHT RAILWAY

Address: Pecorama, Beer, East Devon, EX12 3NA	**N° of Steam Locos:** 8 at present
Telephone N°: (01297) 21542	**N° of Other Locos:** 3
Year Formed: 1975	**Approx N° of Visitors P.A.:** 80,000
Location of Line: Beer, East Devon	**Gauge:** 7¼ inches
Length of Line: 1 mile	**Web site:** www.pecorama.co.uk
	E-mail: pecorama@pecobeer.co.uk

GENERAL INFORMATION

Nearest Mainline Station: Axminster
Nearest Bus Stop: Beer
Car Parking: Available on site
Coach Parking: Available on site
Souvenir Shop(s): Yes
Food & Drinks: Licensed restaurant on site

SPECIAL INFORMATION

In addition to the Railway, Pecorama features a Model Railway Exhibition, childrens activity areas and extensive gardens.

OPERATING INFORMATION

Opening Times: 2019 dates: Daily from 1st April to 3rd November.
Steam Working: On every operating day, weather permitting.
Prices: Adult £11.00
　　　　　Child £9.00 (Under-1s free of charge)
　　　　　Senior Citizens £10.00 (Over-80s free)
The prices shown above include entry to the Gardens, one ride on the railway and entry to the Model Railway Exhibition.

Detailed Directions by Car:
From All Parts: Take the A3052 to Beer, turn onto the B3174 and follow the Brown Tourist signs for Pecorama.

BEKONSCOT LIGHT RAILWAY

Address: Bekonscot Model Village &
Railway, Warwick Road, Beaconsfield,
Bucks   HP9 2PL
Telephone Nº: (01494) 672919
Year Formed: 2001 (Originally 1929)
Location of Line: Beaconsfield, Bucks.
Length of Line: 400 yards

Nº of Steam Locos: None at present
Nº of Other Locos: 3
Approx Nº of Visitors P.A.: 180,000
Gauge: 7¼ inches
Web site: www.bekonscot.co.uk

GENERAL INFORMATION

Nearest Mainline Station: Beaconsfield (5 minutes walk)
Nearest Bus Station: High Wycombe
Car Parking: Limited spaces adjacent to the site
Coach Parking: Limited spaces adjacent to the site
Souvenir Shop(s): Yes
Food & Drinks: Available

SPECIAL INFORMATION

The Railway is situated in Bekonscot Model Village, a 1½ acre miniature landscape of fields, farms, castles, churches, woods and lakes which also contains a model railway.

OPERATING INFORMATION

Opening Times: 2019 dates: Daily from 16th February to 3rd November. Open 10.00am to 5.30pm.
Steam Working: None at present
Prices: Adult £10.90 (£12.00 with Gift Aid)
Child £7.00 (Ages 2–15 years)
Family Tickets £21.80 and £31.00
Concessions £8.75 (£9.70 with Gift Aid)
Ticket prices are reduced between 3.30pm and 5.30pm.
Note: Prices shown above are for entrance into Bekonscot Model Village which is required to visit the railway. Rides are an additional £1.50 per person. Reduced rates are available for groups of 15 or more.

Detailed Directions by Car:
From All Parts: Exit the M40 at Junction 2 taking the A355 then follow the signs for the "Model Village".

BENTLEY MINIATURE RAILWAY

Address: Bentley, Harveys Lane, Ringmer   BN8 5AF
Telephone Nº: 0845 867-2583
Year Formed: 1985
Location of Line: 5 miles North of Lewes
Length of Line: 1 mile

Nº of Steam Locos: Members locos only
Nº of Other Locos: Members locos only
Approx Nº of Visitors P.A.: 10,000
Gauge: 7¼ inches
Web site: www.bentleyrailway.co.uk
E-mail: enquiries@bentleyrailway.co.uk

GENERAL INFORMATION

Nearest Mainline Station: Uckfield (4 miles)
Nearest Bus Station: Uckfield (4 miles)
Car Parking: Free parking available on site
Coach Parking: Free parking available on site
Souvenir Shop(s): None
Food & Drinks: None

SPECIAL INFORMATION

The railway is owned and operated by volunteer members of the Bentley Miniature Railway Ltd and operates a wide variety of locomotives.

OPERATING INFORMATION

Opening Times: Weekends from April to September and Mondays, Wednesdays and Fridays during the East Sussex school holidays.
Trains run from 11.30am to 4.00pm (but 11.00am to 5.00pm during the summer).
Steam Working: Most Sundays.
Prices: £2.00 per ride

Detailed Directions by Car:
From All Parts: Bentley Wildfowl & Motor Museum is located just outside of the village of Shortgate by the B2192 road between Halland (which located by at the junction of the B2192 and A22) and Lewes (A26/A27). The Museum is well-signposted locally from the A22 (Uckfield to Eastbourne), A26 (Uckfield to Lewes) and B2192.

BRIDGEND & DISTRICT M.E.S.

Address: Fountain Road, Aberkenfig, Bridgend   CF32 0EH
Telephone Nº: None
Year Formed: 1984
Location of Line: Tondu, near Bridgend
Length of Line: Over 1,200 metres

Nº of Steam Locos: 8
Nº of Other Locos: 10
Nº of Members: Approximately 45
Approx Nº of Visitors P.A.: 4,000
Gauge: 3½ inches, 5 inches & 7¼ inches
Website: www.bridgendminiaturerailway.com

GENERAL INFORMATION

Nearest Mainline Station: Tondu (1 mile)
Nearest Bus Station: Bridgend (2 miles)
Car Parking: Available on site
Coach Parking: Available on site
Food & Drinks: Available

SPECIAL INFORMATION

A 4-inch scale traction engine is available to give rides on most of the Society's open days.

OPERATING INFORMATION

Opening Times: 2019 dates: 6th April; 4th May; 1st June; 23rd June (Railway & Model Show which has an admission charge and runs from 11.00am to 3.00pm); 6th & 20th July; 3rd & 17th August; 7th September; 5th October; 26th October (for Halloween rides from 4.00pm to 7.00pm); Santa Specials on 14th December (ticket only) and Boxing Day rides from 11.00am to 2.00pm.
Trains run from noon until 4.00pm unless stated.
Steam Working: All open days where possible.
Prices: £2.00 per person per ride.
         6 rides for £10.00
Note: The line is available for birthday party bookings. Please check the web site for details.

Detailed Directions by Car:
Exit the M4 at Junction 36 and follow the A4063 Northwards. At the first roundabout take the 2nd exit onto the B4281 Park Road. Continue into Fountain Road and turn right (still on Fountain Road). The MES club area is located opposite the entrance to Parc Slip Nature Reserve.

BRIGHOUSE & HALIFAX MODEL ENGINEERS

Address: Ravensprings Park, Cawcliffe Road, Brighouse   HD6 2HP
Telephone Nº: (01484) 717140
Year Formed: 1932
Location of Line: Ravensprings Park
Length of Line: 650 feet (5 inch gauge) and 1,200 feet (7¼ inch gauge)

Nº of Steam Locos: 50-60
Nº of Other Locos: 2 (traction engines)
Nº of Members: Approximately 75
Approx Nº of Visitors P.A.: 4,500
Gauge: 2½ inches, 3½ inches, 5 inches and 7¼ inches
Web site: www.bhme.co.uk

GENERAL INFORMATION

Nearest Mainline Station: Brighouse (1½ miles)
Nearest Bus Station: Brighouse (1 mile)
Car Parking: Available on site
Coach Parking: Available by prior arrangement
Food & Drinks: Available on open days

OPERATING INFORMATION

Opening Times: 2019 dates: 14th April; 12th May; 9th & 23rd June; 14th July; 11th August; 8th & 29th September; 13th October.
Trains run from 1.30pm to 5.00pm.
Steam Working: All operating days.
Prices: Adults £3.00 (unlimited rides)
Children £2.00 (unlimited rides)
Concessions £2.00 (unlimited rides)

Detailed Directions by Car:
Ravensprings Park lies in the Northern part of Brighouse. From the South: Take the A641 Bradford Road northwards and turn left just after the Thaal Indian Restaurant into Cross Street for Smith Carr Lane. Turn right into Bracken Road then left into Cawcliffe Road for the Park; From the North: Travel into Brighouse on the A641 and turn right just before the Thaal Indian Restaurant into Cross Street. Then as above.

BROMSGROVE SOCIETY OF MODEL ENGINEERS

Address: Avoncroft Museum of Historic Buildings, Stoke Heath, Bromsgrove, B60 4JR
Phone Nº: (0121) 476-6866 (Secretary)
Year Formed: 1980s
Location: In the grounds of the museum
Length of Line: 1,260 feet

Nº of Steam Locos: Members locos only
Nº of Other Locos: 4 + members locos
Nº of Members: Approximately 50
Approx Nº of Visitors P.A.: Not known
Gauge: 2½ inches, 3½ inches, 5 inches and smaller gauges
Website: www.bromsgrovesme.co.uk

GENERAL INFORMATION

Nearest Mainline Station: Bromsgrove (1.5 miles)
Nearest Bus Station: Stoke Heath
Car Parking: In the Museum car park
Coach Parking: Available
Souvenir Shop(s): In the Museum only
Food & Drinks: Available

OPERATING INFORMATION

Opening Times: Trains run every Tuesday from March to October and also on a number of other Special Event days throughout the year. Please check the web site for further details. Trains run from 10.30am to 5.00pm.
Steam Working: Most operating days
Prices: Adults £11.00
Children £6.00 (Under-5s admitted free)
Senior Citizens £9.90 Students £6.00
Family £33.00
Note: Prices shown are for entrance into the Museum. Train rides are an additional 50p per person.

Detailed Directions by Car:
The track site is adjacent to Avoncroft Museum of Historic Buildings which is situated just off the A38 Bromsgrove bypass. From the South: The Museum is signposted from Junction 5 of the M5; From the North: The Museum is signposted from Junction 1 of the M42. After turning off the road into the museum, the club's private entrance gates are to the left of Avoncroft's main entrance. SatNav users should use B60 4JR as the destination post code.

BROOKSIDE MINIATURE RAILWAY

Address: London Road North (A523), Poynton, Cheshire SK12 1BY
Telephone Nº: 0781 807-0723
Year Formed: 1989
Location: Brookside Garden Centre
Length of Line: Almost ¾ mile

Nº of Steam Locos: Visiting locos only
Nº of Other Locos: 3
Approx Nº of Visitors P.A.: 70,000
Gauge: 7¼ inches
Web: www.brooksideminiaturerailway.co.uk

GENERAL INFORMATION

Nearest Mainline Station: Poynton and Hazel Grove (both 1 mile)
Nearest Bus Station: Stockport (5 miles).
Car Parking: 300 spaces available on site
Coach Parking: 2 spaces available
Souvenir Shop(s): Yes
Food & Drinks: Yes

SPECIAL INFORMATION

The Railway runs through the grounds of the Brookside Garden Centre. There is also an extensive collection of Railwayana on display.

OPERATING INFORMATION

Opening Times: The Railway is open on weekends and Bank Holidays and late night Thursdays from April to September. Open every day in July and August as well as during School holidays. Trains usually run from 10.45am to 4.00pm.
Steam Working: No set dates as it is dependent on visiting locos.
Prices: £2.00 per ride (Under-2s ride for free)
Note: Exceptional rainfall during March 2019, caused flooding at the site, damaging a retaining wall adjacent to the line. It is likely that the railway will only be able to run shorter journeys until this is repaired. Please contact the railway for details.

Detailed Directions by Car:
From the North: Exit the M60 at Junction 1 in Stockport and take the A6 (signposted Buxton). Upon reaching Hazel Grove, take the A523 to Poynton. Follow the brown tourist signs for the Railway; From the West: Exit the M56 at Junction 6 signposted Wilmslow and continue to Poynton. Follow the brown signs for the Railway; From the South: Exit the M6 at Junction 18 for Holmes Chapel. Follow the signs to Wilmslow, then as from the West; From the East: Follow the A6 to Hazel Grove, then as from the North.

BROOMY HILL RAILWAY

Address: Broomy Hill, Hereford
Telephone Nº: 07979 782688
Year Formed: 1962
Location of Line: Adjacent to the
Waterworks Museum, Hereford
Length of Line: Approximately 1 mile

Nº of Steam Locos: 4+
Nº of Other Locos: 2+
Nº of Members: Approximately 120
Approx Nº of Visitors P.A.: Not known
Gauge: 7¼ inches, 5 inches, 3½ inches
Web site: www.hsme.co.uk

GENERAL INFORMATION

Nearest Mainline Station: Hereford (1½ miles)
Nearest Bus Station: Hereford (1½ miles)
Car Parking: Free parking available on site
Coach Parking: Available by prior arrangement
Souvenir Shop(s): Yes
Food & Drinks: Available

SPECIAL INFORMATION

The Broomy Hill Railway is operated by the
Hereford Society of Model Engineers and has two
separate tracks which run along the bank of the
River Wye. Members run their own locomotives so
the number and variety in operation may vary from
day to day. Entry to the site is free of charge and
picnic areas are available.

OPERATING INFORMATION

Opening Times: 2019 dates: 7th, 21st & 22nd April;
12th, 26th & 27th May; 9th & 23rd June;
7th & 28th July; 11th, 25th & 26th August;
8th & 29th September; 13th & 26th October.
Trains run from 12.00pm to 4.30pm (2.00pm to
6.00pm for the Halloween trains on 26th October).
Steam Working: All operating days.
Prices: Adults £1.50 per ride
          Children £1.50 per ride
Note: Four rides can be bought for £5.00 and
children's parties can be arranged. Also, the site is
prone to flooding so open days may sometimes be
cancelled following heavy rainfall.

Detailed Directions by Car:
From the centre of Hereford, take the A49 Ross-on-Wye Road, turning right into Barton Road. After approximately
400 metres, turn left into Broomy Hill Road, proceed for around 600 metres before turning left following signs
for the Waterworks Museum. The railway is on the right just after the museum which is signposted with Brown
Tourist Information Signs.

BURNLEY & PENDLE MINIATURE RAILWAY (THOMPSON PARK RAILWAY)

Location: Thompson Park, Colne Road, Burnley BB11 2AA	**Nº of Steam Locos**: 3 (Member's locos)
Contact Telephone Nº: 07957 714148	**Nº of Other Locos**: 10
Year Formed: 1990	**Nº of Members**: 36
Length of Line: 1 kilometre	**Annual Membership Fee**: £10.00
Gauge: 7¼ inches	**Approx Nº of Visitors P.A.**: 22,000
	Website: www.thompsonparkrailway.co.uk
	Facebook page: 'Thompson Park Railway'

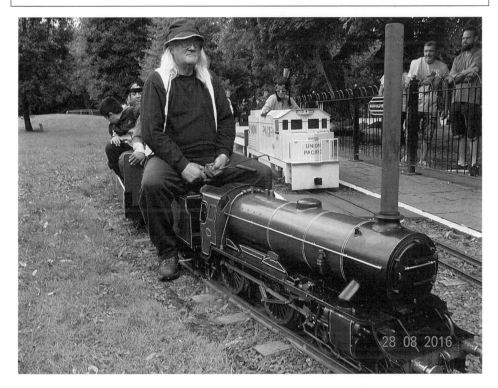

GENERAL INFORMATION

Nearest Mainline Station: Burnley Central (1 mile)
Nearest Bus Station: Burnley (1 mile)
Car Parking: A Pay and Display car park is planned to be in place during Easter 2019.
Coach Parking: Not available
Food & Drinks: Available from a kiosk in the Park

OPERATING INFORMATION

Opening Times: Weekends and Bank Holidays from March until the end of October. Also on Wednesdays during the School Holidays. Special events are held on the last Sunday in April, July and August. Please check the facebook page for details. Trains run between 12.00pm and 4.00pm.
Steam Working: Most operating days.
Prices: £1.00 per person per ride
£10.00 for 12 rides
Note: Dogs are not allowed in Thompson Park.

Detailed Directions by Car:
The Railway runs through Thompson Park in Burnley. The pedestrian entrance is in Ormerod Road, just a short distance from the town centre and also near to Turf Moor, the home of Burnley FC. Cars enter via Colne Road.

CAMBRIDGE & DISTRICT MODEL ENGINEERING SOCIETY

Address: Fulbrooke Road, Cambridge, CB3 9EE	**Nº of Steam Locos:** 12
Telephone Nº: none	**Nº of Other Locos:** 4
Year Formed: 1938	**Nº of Members:** 90
Location of Line: Newnham, Cambridge	**Approx Nº of Visitors P.A.:** 3,500
Length of Line: ¾ mile	**Gauge:** 3½ inches, 5 inches and 7¼ inches
	Web site: www.cambridgemes.co.uk

GENERAL INFORMATION

Nearest Mainline Station: Cambridge (2 miles)
Nearest Bus Station: Drummer Street (1 mile)
Car Parking: Available on site (no street parking)
Coach Parking: None
Souvenir Shop(s): None
Food & Drinks: Cafe open on operating days

SPECIAL INFORMATION

The Cambridge & District MES was formed in 1938 and the track and clubhouse in Fulbrooke Road was constructed on a 2 acre site during 1959.

OPERATING INFORMATION

Opening Times: 2019 dates: Open the 2nd Sunday of the month from April to October inclusive. Gates open at 12.30pm and trains operate from 1.30pm to 5.30pm.
Steam Working: Every operating day.
Prices: Adults £1.50 per ride (4 rides for £5.00)
Concessions £1.50 per ride (4 rides for £5)
Children £1.50 per ride (4 rides for £5.00)
Note: Under-5s must be accompanied by an adult and Under-3s ride free of charge.

Detailed Directions by Car:
The Railway is located in the south-western part of Cambridge in the suburb of Newnham, just behind the ground of Cambridge Rugby Club. Exit the M11 at Junction 12 and follow the A603 (Barton Road) into Cambridge. After approximately 1½ miles, turn right into Grantchester Road. Car parking for the railway is signposted from Grantchester Road and is normally at the Rugby Club itself.

CANTERBURY & DISTRICT M.E.S.

Address: Brett Quarry, Fordwich, Near Canterbury, Kent **Phone Nº**: 0774 101-2004 (Vice chairman) **Year Formed**: 1972 **Location of Line**: Brett Quarry, Fordwich **Length of Line**: 750 feet	**Nº of Steam Locos**: (As provided by the **Nº of Other Locos**: MES members) **Nº of Members**: Approximately 70 **Annual Membership Fee**: £28.00 **Gauge**: 3½ inches and 5 inches **Web site**: www.cdmes.org

GENERAL INFORMATION

Nearest Mainline Station: Sturry (½ mile)
Nearest Bus Station: Canterbury (3 miles)
Car Parking: None on site
Coach Parking: None
Food & Drinks: None

SPECIAL INFORMATION

The Canterbury & District Model Engineering Society runs a track on land kindly loaned by Bretts of Fordwich which is open to the public on some Sunday afternoons throughout the year, weather permitting.

OPERATING INFORMATION

Opening Times: 2019 dates: 14th April; 12th May; 9th June; 14th July; 8th September; 13th October. Trains run from 2.00pm onwards, weather permitting.
Steam Working: Most operating days depending on which locos have been provided by the MES members.
Prices: Free rides although donations are accepted for the upkeep of the track.

Detailed Directions by Car:
From the A28 at Sturry turn into Fordwich Road then left into Marlowe Meadows (look for the Brett sign). Drive towards the large green gates then walk through following the access road. Please note that the railway is on private land and access to the public is limited so please do not drive down this road as there is no parking on-site.

CANVEY MINIATURE RAILWAY

Address: Waterside Farm Sports Centre, Somnes Avenue, Canvey Island   SS8 9RA
Telephone N°: Please check the web site for contact information
Year Formed: 1976
Location of Line: Canvey Island
Length of Line: Two lines, one of 1,440 feet and one of 4,400 feet (7¼ inch line)

N° of Steam Locos: Variable
N° of Other Locos: Variable
N° of Members: Approximately 80
Approx N° of Visitors P.A.: 6,000
Gauge: 3½ inches, 5 inches & 7¼ inches
Web site: www.cramec.org

GENERAL INFORMATION

Nearest Mainline Station: Benfleet (1 mile)
Nearest Bus Station: Bus stop just outside
Car Parking: Available on site
Coach Parking: Available on site
Food & Drinks: None

SPECIAL INFORMATION

The railway is operated by members of the Canvey Railway and Model Engineering Club.

OPERATING INFORMATION

Opening Times: 2019 dates: Every Sunday from 7th April until 13th October. Also open for Santa Specials on dates on 1st and 8th December. Please contact the railway for further information. Trains run from 10.30am to 3.45pm, weather permitting.
Steam Working: When available on operating days.
Prices: £1.00 per ride.
   Also £5.00 for 6 rides or £9.00 for 12 rides.
Note: Higher prices apply for Santa Specials.

Detailed Directions by Car:
All road routes to Canvey Island meet at the Waterside Farm roundabout. The railway lines are located in the grounds of the Sports Complex/Leisure Centre. Turn right at the traffic lights into the centre and the car park is on the left with the railway on the right.

CARDIFF MODEL ENGINEERING SOCIETY

Address: King George V Drive East,
Heath Park, Cardiff   CF14 4AW
Telephone Nº: (029) 2025-5000
Year Formed: 1948
Location of Line: Heath Park, Cardiff
Length of Line: 2 tracks of 1,000 feet
each plus a tram track of 700 feet

Nº of Steam Locos: 8   (plus many
Nº of Other Locos: 4   members locos)
Nº of Members: Approximately 190
Approx Nº of Visitors P.A.: 12,000
Gauge: 3½ inches, 5 inches & 7¼ inches
Web site: www.cardiffmes.com

GENERAL INFORMATION

Nearest Mainline Station: Heath Low Level (½ mile)
Nearest Bus Stop: Allensbank Road
Car Parking: Available on site and also nearby
Coach Parking: None
Food & Drinks: Available

SPECIAL INFORMATION

The Cardiff Model Engineering society moved to
Heath Park in 1987. The site, which includes two
railway tracks and a unique electric tramway, an '00'
gauge model railway, a garden railway catering for
32mm & 45mm gauges and extensive refreshment
facilities, has been developed by the members for the
benefit of visitors.

OPERATING INFORMATION

Opening Times: 2019 public running days: 7th,
21st & 22nd April; 26th & 27th May; 23rd June;
21st July; 25th & 26th August; 22nd September;
6th October. Trains run from 1.00pm to 5.00pm.
Steam Working: All operating days.
Prices: £2.00 entry per person then £2.00 per ride.
Children aged 3 and under are admitted and ride
free of charge.

Detailed Directions by Car:
Exit the M4 at Junction 32 and travel towards Cardiff. Turn left at the 3rd set of traffic lights (by the Tesco garage)
and continue through 3 sets of traffic lights to the T-junction lights. Turn left here then immediately right then
take the 1st left onto King George V Drive. Turn left at the roundabout and take the lane 400 yards on the right.

CHELMSFORD SOCIETY OF MODEL ENGINEERS

Address: Meteor Way (off Waterhouse Lane), Chelmsford, Essex   CM1 2RL
Telephone Nº: None
Year Formed: 1935
Location of Line: Chelmsford
Length of Line: Two tracks, each approximately 1,000 feet long
Web site: www.chelmsfordsocietyofmodelengineers.org.uk

Nº of Steam Locos: 40+   (owned by
Nº of Other Locos: 20+   members)
Nº of Members: Approximately 100
Approx Nº of Visitors P.A.: 1,500
Gauge: 3½ inches, 5 inches & 7¼ inches

GENERAL INFORMATION

Nearest Mainline Station: Chelmsford (½ mile)
Nearest Bus Station: Chelmsford (½ mile)
Car Parking: Available adjacent to the railway (currently free of charge at weekends)
Food & Drinks: Light refreshments available

SPECIAL INFORMATION

The Chelmsford Society of Model Engineers promotes the safe construction and operation of passenger-carrying steam, electric and diesel hauled trains, traction engines and other scale models.

OPERATING INFORMATION

Opening Times: 2019 dates: Every Sunday from 28th April to 6th October inclusive. Santa Specials operate on 8th December. Trains usually run from 2.00pm to 4.30pm on running dates.
A number of Special Events are held during the year. Please check the Society's web site for further details.
Steam Working: Most operating days.
Prices: £1.50 per ride or £5.00 for 6 rides.

Detailed Directions by Car:
From London: Follow the A12 then take the A1016 towards Chelmsford town centre. Continue past the A414 junctions into Westway then into Waterhouse Lane. Meteor Way is on the right after the fourth set of traffic lights, just before the river. Park and then proceed past the five bar gate to the club entrance on the right; From Southend: Follow the A130 to the A12 junction then cross onto the A1114. After 1¼ miles join the A414 towards Chelmsford. Follow the A414 around Chelmsford to the junction with the A1016 at Widford. Take the 2nd exit into Westway then as from London; From Colchester: Follow the A12 and exit at the A414 junction towards Chelmsford. Follow the A414 to the A1016, then as from Southend.

CHINGFORD & DISTRICT M.E.C.

Address: Ridgeway Park, Peel Close,
Old Church Road, Chingford   E4 6XU
Telephone Nº: None
Year Formed: 1945
Location: Ridgeway Park, Chingford
Length of Lines: 1,000 feet (5 inch track)
and 3,000 feet (7¼ inch track)
Web site: www.chingford-model-engineering.com

Nº of Steam Locos: 11 (owned by Club)
Nº of Other Locos: Many
Nº of Members: 100+
Annual Membership Fee: £25.00 Adult
Approx Nº of Visitors P.A.: 17,000
Gauge: 3½ inches, 5 inches & 7¼ inches

GENERAL INFORMATION

Nearest Mainline Station: Chingford (1½ miles)
Nearest Underground Station: Walthamstow
Central (5 miles)
Car Parking: Limited spaces within the Park
Coach Parking: None
Food & Drinks: None

SPECIAL INFORMATION

The Chingford & District Model Engineering Club
seeks to promote all forms of model engineering
and model making. It's members come from all
walks of life, and do not necessarily have an
engineering background.

OPERATING INFORMATION

Opening Times: 2019 dates: Sundays and Bank
Holidays from 7th April to 6th October inclusive
and also on Wednesdays during August.
Train rides usually run from 2.00pm to 5.30pm.
Steam Working: Practically every operating day.
Prices: £1.00 per person per ride on the raised track
          £1.50 per person per ride on the ground track
Note: The Railway is available to hire for children's
parties during the summer months.

Detailed Directions by Car:
Ridgeway Park is situated off the A112 Old Church Road in Chingford. Turn into Peel Close and the Park entrance
is on the left after 50 yards at the mini-roundabout. A small car park is situated in Ridgeway Park. The railway
itself is located about 150 yards down the main path on the right.

COATE WATER PARK MINIATURE RAILWAY

Address: Coate Water Country Park, Swindon, Wiltshire   SN3 6AA
Telephone Nº: (01666) 577596 (Secretary)
Year Formed: 1964
Location of Line: Coate Water Country Park, Swindon
Length of Line: ¾ mile (1,250 metres)

Nº of Steam/Other Locos: A number of different locos are supplied for use by members of the Society
Nº of Members: Approximately 70
Approx Nº of Visitors P.A.: 26,000
Gauge: 5 inches and 7¼ inches
Web site: www.nwmes.info

GENERAL INFORMATION

Nearest Mainline Station: Swindon (2 miles)
Nearest Bus Station: Swindon (2 miles)
Car Parking: Available in the Park
Coach Parking: None
Food & Drinks: Available in the Park

SPECIAL INFORMATION

The Coate Water Park Miniature Railway is operated by the North Wilts Model Engineering Society.

OPERATING INFORMATION

Opening Times: Sundays, Bank Holiday Mondays and some Saturdays. Open from 11.00am with trains running until approximately 5.00pm in the summer months, weather permitting.
Please contact the railway for further information.
Steam Working: Depends which locos have been provided for use on the day by the individual members.
Prices: £2.00 per person per ride.

Detailed Directions by Car:
From Junction 15 of the M4, take the A419 North. Take the first exit left onto the A4259 towards Swindon and follow the dual-carriageway past the Great Western Hospital then turn left at the roundabout for Coate Water Park and follow the road to the main car park. From the car park walk round to the left for the railway.

CONWY VALLEY RAILWAY MUSEUM

Address: Old Goods Yard, Betws-y-Coed, Conwy, North Wales LL24 0AL **Telephone Nº**: (01690) 710568 **Year Formed**: 1983 **Location of Line**: Betws-y-Coed **Length of Line**: One and an eighth miles	**Nº of Steam Locos**: 2 **Nº of Other Locos**: 2 **Approx Nº of Visitors P.A.**: 50,000 **Gauge**: 7¼ inches and 15 inches **Web**: www.conwyrailwaymuseum.co.uk

GENERAL INFORMATION

Nearest Mainline Station: Betws-y-Coed (20 yards)
Nearest Bus Station: 40 yards
Car Parking: Car park at site
Coach Parking: Car park at site
Souvenir Shop(s): Yes
Food & Drinks: Yes – Buffet Coach Cafe

SPECIAL INFORMATION

The Museum houses the unique 3D dioramas by the late Jack Nelson. Also the ¼ size steam loco 'Britannia'. A steam service is provided by two locos built at the Museum, the newest of which is Fairlie loco 'Geirionydd', completed in September 2017.

OPERATING INFORMATION

Opening Times: Daily from 10.00am to 5.00pm.
Trains Working: Daily from 10.15am
Prices: Adult – £1.50 museum entry
          Child/Senior Citizen – £1.00 museum entry
          Family tickets – £4.00 museum entry
          Train Rides £2.00 per person
Note: Tram rides are usually available on a 15 inch gauge single-deck tram using a specially-built ½ mile track running alongside the mainline.
'Toby', a self-drive electric tram for children runs on a 7¼ inch gauge track by the Coach Cafe.

Detailed Directions by Car:
From Midlands & South: Take M54/M6 onto the A5 and into Betws-y-Coed; From Other Parts: Take the A55 coast road then the A470 to Betws-y-Coed. The museum is located by the Mainline Station directly off the A5.

CROWBOROUGH MINIATURE RAILWAY

Address: Goldsmiths Leisure Centre, Eridge Road, Crowborough TN6 2TN	**Nº of Steam Locos:** Members locos only
Telephone Nº: (01892) 852741	**Nº of Other Locos:** 1
Year Formed: 1990	**Nº of Members:** 30
Location of Line: Crowborough	**Approx Nº of Visitors P.A.:** 1,500
Length of Line: 1,000 feet	**Gauge:** 3½ inches, 5 inches & 7¼ inches
Web site: www.crowboroughminiaturerailway.com	

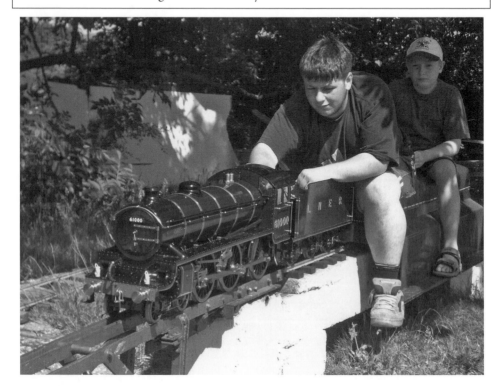

GENERAL INFORMATION

Nearest Mainline Station: Crowborough (1½ miles)
Nearest Bus Station: Tunbridge Wells (7 miles)
Car Parking: Available on site
Coach Parking: Available on site
Food & Drinks: Available at the Leisure Centre

SPECIAL INFORMATION

The Crowborough Locomotive Society was formed to build, maintain, and run a miniature railway at the Goldsmiths Leisure Centre in Crowborough. The society runs live steam working locomotives to give both young and old alike a railway journey in miniature!

OPERATING INFORMATION

Opening Times: Saturday afternoons and Bank Holidays from Easter until 7th December. A Special Bonfire Night event is held on 5th November and Santa Specials run on 14th December.
Trains run from 2.00pm to 5.00pm.
Steam Working: Most operational days, depending on which members' locos are running.
Prices: £1.00 for one circuit of the extended track
Note: Birthday parties can be held at the railway by prior arrangement.

Detailed Directions by Car:
Goldsmiths Leisure Centre is situated in the north of Crowborough just off the A26 (Eridge Road) which is the main Tunbridge Wells to Uckfield through road.

CUTTESLOWE PARK MINIATURE RAILWAY

Address: Cutteslowe Park, Harbord Road, Oxford   OX2 8ES
(SatNav OX2 8LH – House Number 41!)
Phone Nº: 07900 972380 (Secretary)
Year Formed: 1955
Location: Cutteslowe Park, Oxford
Length of Line: Two lines – 390 yard raised line and 500 yard ground level line

Nº of Steam Locos: 40
Nº of Other Locos: 15
Nº of Members: Approximately 110
Annual Membership Fee: £40.00 (Adult)
Approx Nº of Visitors P.A.: 30,000
Gauge: 3½ inches, 5 inches & 7¼ inches
Web site: www.cosme.org.uk

GENERAL INFORMATION

Nearest Mainline Station: Oxford (3¼ miles)
Nearest Bus Station: Oxford (3 miles)
Car Parking: Available on site
Coach Parking: Available by prior arrangement
Food & Drinks: Refreshments are available in Cutteslowe Park

SPECIAL INFORMATION

The Cutteslowe Park Miniature Railway is operated by the City of Oxford Society of Model Engineers.

OPERATING INFORMATION

Opening Times: 2019 dates: Every 1st, 3rd and occasional 5th Sunday from 7th April to 27th October inclusive. Also open on Bank Holidays from April to the end of October and on Wednesday afternoons during the summer holidays. Trains run from 1.30pm to 5.00pm (4.30pm in October).
Steam Working: Up to 5 steam locomotives run on every operating day.
Prices: £1.25 per ride (Under-2s ride free)
      10 rides are available for £10.00

Detailed Directions by Car:
From outside of Oxford join the ringroad and head to the North of the city. At the roundabout at the junction of the A40 ringroad and the A4165 Banbury Road, head North signposted for Kidlington. Take the third turn on the right into Harbord Road which leads directly into the Park. Follow the signs from the car park for the Railway.

DEVON RAILWAY CENTRE

Address: Bickleigh, Tiverton, Devon, EX16 8RG	**Nº of Steam Locos**: 1
Telephone Nº: (01884) 855671	**Nº of Other Locos**: 12
Year Formed: 1997	**Approx Nº of Visitors P.A.**: Not recorded
Location of Line: Bickleigh, Devon	**Gauge**: 2 feet, 7¼ inches and Standard
Length of Line: ½ mile (2 foot and 7¼ inch gauges); 200 yards (Standard gauge)	**Web site**: www.devonrailwaycentre.co.uk
	E-mail: devonrailway@btinternet.com

GENERAL INFORMATION

Nearest Mainline Station: Exeter
Nearest Bus Station: Tiverton (Route 55)
Car Parking: Available on site
Coach Parking: Available on site
Souvenir Shop(s): Yes
Food & Drinks: Yes

SPECIAL INFORMATION

Devon Railway Centre has passenger carrying lines and also features a large model railway exhibition with 15 working layouts. A delightful Edwardian model village built to a 1:12 scale has recently been extended with a model funfair added and a new museum coach opened recently.

OPERATING INFORMATION

Opening Times: 2019 dates: Daily from 6th to 28th April, 22nd May to 8th September and 19th to 27th October. Closed on Mondays in June. Open Wednesday to Sunday inclusive from 1st to 26th May and 11th to 29th September. Also open during weekends in October. Open from 10.30am until 5.00pm on all operating days.
Steam Working: Please phone or e-mail for details.
Prices: Adult £8.80   Child £7.80
               Senior Citizen £8.00   Family £31.20
Admission includes unlimited train rides and access to the model village, model railways, museum and crazy golf.

Detailed Directions by Car:
From All Parts: Devon Railway Centre is situated adjacent to the famous Bickleigh Bridge, just off the A396 Exeter to Tiverton road (3 miles from Tiverton and 8 miles from Exeter).

DRAGON MINIATURE RAILWAY

Address: Marple Garden Centre, Dooley Lane, Marple, Stockport SK6 7HE **Telephone Nº**: 07748 581160 **Year Formed**: 1999 **Location of Line**: Marple Garden Centre **Length of Line**: ½ mile	**Nº of Steam Locos**: 7 **Nº of Other Locos**: 5 **Approx Nº of Visitors P.A.**: 30,000 **Gauge**: 7¼ inches **Web**: www.freewebs.com/dragonrailway/ **E-mail**: dragonrailway@hotmail.co.uk

GENERAL INFORMATION

Nearest Mainline Station: Romley (1 mile)
Nearest Bus Station: Stockport (2½ miles)
Car Parking: Available on site
Coach Parking: Available
Souvenir Shop(s): Yes
Food & Drinks: Available

SPECIAL INFORMATION

Dragon Miniature Railway is one of the few Garden Centre-based railways which operates steam on most open days.

OPERATING INFORMATION

Opening Times: Weekends and Bank Holidays and also daily during local school holidays throughout the year. Trains run from 11.00am to 4.30pm, weather permitting.
Steam Working: Most operating days.
Prices: £1.00 per ride (Under-2s free of charge)
Ten-ride tickets are available for £8.00

Detailed Directions by Car:
From All Parts: Exit the M60 at Junction 25, pass through Bredbury and follow signs for Marple along the A627. Cross over the River Goyt and Marple Garden Centre is on the left.

EASTBOURNE MINIATURE STEAM RAILWAY

Address: Lottbridge Drove, Eastbourne, East Sussex BN23 6QJ
Telephone Nº: (01323) 520229
Year Formed: 1992
Location of Line: Eastbourne
Length of Line: 1 mile

Nº of Steam Locos: 8
Nº of Other Locos: 3
Approx Nº of Visitors P.A.: Not known
Gauge: 7¼ inches
Web site: www.emsr.co.uk

GENERAL INFORMATION

Nearest Mainline Station: Eastbourne (2 miles)
Nearest Bus Station: Eastbourne (2 miles)
Car Parking: Free parking on site
Coach Parking: Free parking on site
Souvenir Shop(s): Yes
Food & Drinks: Yes

SPECIAL INFORMATION

The Railway site also has many other attractions including model railways, an adventure playground, maze, nature walk, picnic area and a Cafe.

OPERATING INFORMATION

Opening Times: 2019 dates: Daily from 6th April until 3rd November. Trains run from 10.00am to 5.00pm during these days.
Steam Working: Weekends, Bank Holidays and during School Holidays. Diesel at other times.
Prices: Adult £5.50
Child £5.00 (Under-3s ride free)
Family Tickets £19.00
(2 adults + 2 children)

Detailed Directions by Car:
From All Parts: Take the A22 new road to Eastbourne then follow the Brown tourist signs for the 'Mini Railway'.

EAST HERTS MINIATURE RAILWAY

Address: Van Hage Garden Centre, Great Amwell, near Ware SG12 9RP	**Nº of Steam Locos**: 4
Telephone Nº: (020) 8292-2997	**Nº of Other Locos**: 4
Year Formed: 1978	**Nº of Members**: Approximately 40
Location: Van Hage Garden Centre	**Annual Membership Fee**: £16.00
Length of Line: 500 metres	**Approx Nº of Visitors P.A.**: 40,000
	Gauge: 7¼ inches
	Web site: www.ehmr.org.uk

GENERAL INFORMATION

Nearest Mainline Station: Ware (1½ miles)
Nearest Bus Station: Bus stop outside the Centre
Car Parking: Available on site
Coach Parking: Available
Food & Drinks: Available in the Garden Centre

SPECIAL INFORMATION

The Railway operates a line at the Van Hage Garden Centre in Great Amwell. The railway is run by volunteers and any profits are donated to the local special needs school and other local charities.

OPERATING INFORMATION

Opening Times: Weekends and Bank Holidays throughout the year. Also open Tuesdays and Thursdays during the school holidays. Usually open from 11.00am to 5.00pm but from 10.30am to 4.30pm on Sundays.
Steam Working: Most operating days.
Prices: £1.00 per person per ride. Under-2s travel free of charge and Under-8s must be accompanied by an older, fare-paying passenger.

Detailed Directions by Car:
From the South: Take the A10 towards Cambridge and exit at the first Ware junction signposted for A414. Take the 2nd exit at the roundabout onto the A1170 towards Ware and Van Hage Garden Centre is on the left after 600 metres; From the East: Take the A414 from Harlow and turn off onto the A1170 for Ware. Then as above.

EVERGREENS MINIATURE RAILWAY

Address: Dawn Bank, Keal Cotes,
Lincolnshire   PE23 4AE
Telephone Nº: (01754) 830574 or
(01205) 480703
Year Formed: 2002
Location: Keal Coates, just off the A16
Web site: www.evergreensminiaturerailway.org
E-mail: evergreensminiaturerailway@gmail.com

Nº of Steam Locos: 10
Nº of Other Locos: 14
Nº of Members: 32
Approx Nº of Visitors P.A.: Not known
Gauge: 5 inches and 7¼ inches

This photograph shown above is of the old site in Stickney.

GENERAL INFORMATION

Nearest Mainline Station: Boston (12 miles)
Nearest Bus Station: Spilsby (4 miles)
Car Parking: Available on site
Coach Parking: None
Food & Drinks: Available

SPECIAL INFORMATION

Originally based in Stickney, the Railway has
recently had to relocate to a new site in Keal Cotes.
The new site is a 4½ acre field which has been
named Dawn Bank and members hope to have a
basic track up and running during 2019.

OPERATING INFORMATION

Opening Times: Trains would normally operate on
the last Saturday of the month from April to October
as well as New Year's Day and Easter Saturday with
trains running from 10.30am to 4.00pm. However,
as the track on the new site is not yet up and
running, no operational dates have yet been set for
2019. Please check the web site for further news.
Steam Working: Most operating days.
Prices: Admission £3.00
            Family tickets £8.00 (2 adults + 2 children)
Note: The prices shown include unlimited rides.

Detailed Directions by Car:
The railway is situated in Keal Cotes, on the A16 between Boston and Spilsby. Upon reaching Keal Cotes, turn into
Fen Road opposite The Coach House pub. Continue along Fen Road to the East Fen Catchwater Drain bridge and
turn right immediately after crossing the bridge. Dawn Bank is along this road.

FRIMLEY LODGE MINIATURE RAILWAY

Address: Frimley Lodge Park, Sturt Road, Frimley Green, Surrey   GU16 6HT
Phone No: 07710 606461 (Please use on operating days only)
Year Formed: 1991
Location of Line: Frimley Green
Length of Line: 1 kilometre

No of Steam Locos: 5 (Members' locos)
No of Other Locos: 3
No of Members: Approximately 60
Approx No of Visitors P.A.: 20,000+
Gauge: 3½ inches, 5 inches & 7¼ inches
Web site: www.flmr.org

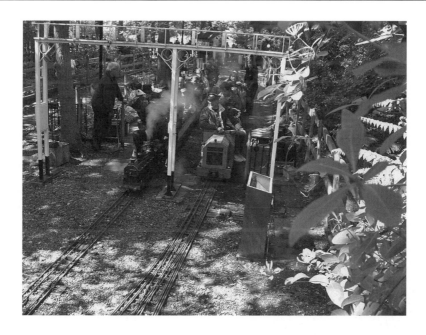

GENERAL INFORMATION

Nearest Mainline Station: Frimley or Ashvale (both 2 miles)
Nearest Bus Station: Farnborough (4 miles) – Take the Number 3 bus between Aldershot and Yately.
Car Parking: Available on site
Coach Parking: Available by prior arrangement
Food & Drinks: Cafe in the Park

SPECIAL INFORMATION

The Railway is operated by volunteers from the Frimley and Ascot Locomotive Club who bring their own Locomotives to give pleasure to others. All the proceeds are used for the maintenance of the Railway and to benefit local charities.

OPERATING INFORMATION

Opening Times: 2019 dates: The first Sunday of the month from March to November. Also on 18th May and 26th August. Halloween trains run on 2nd November (5.30pm to 7.30pm pre-booking required) and Santa Specials run on 8th December 11.30am to 2.30pm, also by pre-booked tickets. Trains run from 11.00am to 5.00pm on Sundays and from 11.00am to 1.00pm then 2.00pm to 4.00pm on Wednesdays during the school holidays.
Steam Working: Operational Sundays only.
Prices: Single Rides £1.50
           Family Ticket £10.00 (14 rides)

Detailed Directions by Car:
Exit the M3 at Junction 4 and take the A331 towards Guildford. Leave the A331 at the turn-off for Mytchett and turn left at the top of the ramp then left again at the Miners Arms into Sturt Road. Cross over the bridge then turn right into Frimley Lodge Park. Once in the Park turn right then right again then take the next left for the Railway.

GOLDING SPRING MINIATURE RAILWAY

Address: Quainton Road Station, Quainton, Aylesbury, Bucks. HP22 4BY	**N° of Steam Locos**: 12
Phone N°: (01296) 623540 (Secretary)	**N° of Other Locos**: 4
Year Formed: 1972	**N° of Members**: Approximately 120
Location: Within the Buckinghamshire Railway Centre site	**Approx N° of Visitors P.A.**: 25,000
	Gauge: 3½ inches, 5 inches & 7¼ inches
Length of Line: 1,200 yards	**Web site**: www.vames.org.uk

GENERAL INFORMATION

Nearest Mainline Station: Aylesbury (6 miles)
Nearest Bus Station: Aylesbury (6 miles)
Car Parking: Free parking for 500 cars available
Coach Parking: Free parking for 10 coaches
Souvenir Shop(s): Yes
Food & Drinks: Yes

SPECIAL INFORMATION

The Golding Spring Miniature Railway is operated by members of the Vale of Aylesbury Model Engineering Society and is located at the Buckinghamshire Railway Centre. Other attractions include a 32mm and 45mm Garden Railway.

OPERATING INFORMATION

Opening Times: Sundays and Bank Holidays from March to October inclusive. Also on Wednesdays in the school holidays to coincide with the Bucks Railway Centre. Trains run from 10.30am to 5.30pm
Steam Working: Every operational day.
Prices: £1.00 per ride
Under-3s travel free of charge

Detailed Directions by Car:
The Buckinghamshire Railway Centre is signposted off the A41 Aylesbury to Bicester Road at Waddesdon and off the A413 Buckingham to Aylesbury road at Whitchurch. Junctions 7, 8 and 9 of the M40 are all close by.

GREAT COCKCROW RAILWAY

Address: Hardwick Lane, Lyne, near Chertsey, Surrey KT16 0AD
Telephone Nº: (01932) 565474 (Sundays)
Year Formed: 1968
Location of Line: Lyne, near Chertsey
Length of Line: 2 miles

Nº of Steam Locos: Approximately 25
Nº of Other Locos: 3
Approx Nº of Visitors P.A.: 10,000
Gauge: 7¼ inches
Web site: www.cockcrow.co.uk

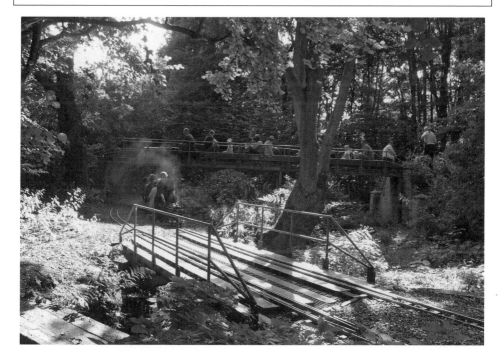

GENERAL INFORMATION

Nearest Mainline Station: Chertsey (30 min. walk)
Nearest Bus Stop: Chertsey (30 minute walk)
Car Parking: Available on site
Coach Parking: Limited parking available on site
Souvenir Shop(s): None
Food & Drinks: Available

SPECIAL INFORMATION

Emanating from the Greywood Central Railway, built from 1946, at a private address in Walton-on-Thames, the Great Cockcrow Railway opened in 1968 and has continually grown since moving to its present site. The Railway offers a choice of two regular routes, each served every few minutes.

OPERATING INFORMATION

Opening Times: 2019 dates: Sundays from 5th May to 27th October when trains run from 1.00pm to 4.30pm. Also open on Wednesdays in August (1.00pm to 4.00pm) and on Halloween Saturday 26th October (5.00pm to 8.00pm).
Steam Working: Every operating day.
Prices: Various combinations of tickets are available ranging from £4.00 for a child to £22.00 for a family double return.

Detailed Directions by Car:
Exit the M25 at Junction 11 and take the A320 towards Woking. At the first roundabout take the exit towards Chertsey and continue along this road passing St. Peter's Hospital on the left, then turn next left (B386) towards Windlesham. Turn right almost immediately into Hardwick Lane and the railway on the right after about ¼ mile just after Hardwick Farm.   Satellite Navigation: KT16 0AD

GRIMSBY & CLEETHORPES M.E.S.

Address: Waltham Windmill Site, Brigsley Road, Waltham, Grimsby   DN32 0JZ
Telephone Nº: None
Year Formed: 1935
Location: Waltham, near Grimsby
Length of Line: 1,300 feet for 7¼ and 5 inch gauges, 600 feet for 3½ gauge

Nº of Steam Locos: 1 (+ members' locos)
Nº of Other Locos: 2
Nº of Members: Approximately 80
Approx Nº of Visitors P.A.: 10,000
Gauge: 3½ inches, 5 inches & 7¼ inches
Web site: www.gcmes.com

GENERAL INFORMATION

Nearest Mainline Station: Grimsby Town (3 miles)
Nearest Bus Station: Grimsby (3 miles)
Car Parking: Available on site
Coach Parking: Limited space available but can be accommodated
Food & Drinks: Available at the Windmill site

SPECIAL INFORMATION

The Society's track is based in Waltham, on the outskirts of Grimsby, next to a preserved windmill dating back to 1878 (the third built on the site since 1666!) which still operates from time to time.

OPERATING INFORMATION

Opening Times: 2019 dates: Sundays and Bank Holidays from 25th March to 27th October. Trains run from 12.00pm to 4.00pm (10.00am when the Windmill Preservation Society holds special events). A special three-day open gala is held over the August Bank Holiday weekend. The railway also runs on Boxing Day and New Year's Day, offering free train rides from 11.00am to 3.00pm. Please check the web site for further details.
Steam Working: Most operating days.
Prices: From 70p per ride

Detailed Directions by Car:
The Railway is situated by Waltham Windmill on the B1203 Grimsby to Binbrook Road and is well signposted. The B1203 connects to the A16 at Scartho, a suburb of Grimsby, about a mile from the railway or to the A18 at Ashby Top, about 3 miles away.

GROSVENOR PARK MINIATURE RAILWAY

Address: Grosvenor Park, Chester, CH1 1QQ	**Nº of Steam Locos**: None at present
Telephone Nº: 07530 397079	**Nº of Other Locos**: 2
Year Formed: 1996	**Approx Nº of Visitors P.A.**: 60,000
Length of Line: ¼ mile	**Gauge**: 7¼ inches
	Web site: None

GENERAL INFORMATION

Nearest Mainline Station: Chester (¾ mile)
Nearest Bus Station: Chester (½ mile)
Car Parking: Park & Ride or Public car parks only
Coach Parking: None
Souvenir Shop(s): Yes
Food & Drinks: Available in the Park Cafe

SPECIAL INFORMATION

Grosvenor Park railway was built in 1996 to commemorate the centenary of the Duke of Westminster's railway at nearby Eaton Hall and is located just a few minutes walk from Chester's historic city centre.

OPERATING INFORMATION

Opening Times: Weekends throughout the year and daily during the school holidays (except Christmas Day). Also on Tuesdays and Thursdays from May to July from 12.00pm to 4.30pm. Otherwise, trains run from 10.30am to 5.00pm at weekends and during the school holidays (11.00am to 4.00pm during the Winter months).
Steam Working: None at present.
Prices: Adults £1.50 (3 ride tickets £2.75)
Children £1.00 (3 ride tickets £1.75)
Family £3.50 (3 ride tickets £7.00)

Detailed Directions by Car:
From All Parts: Grosvenor Park is situated in the centre of Chester, by Grosvenor Park Road and about 400 yards from the City Centre. The Roman Amphitheatre is adjacent to the Park.

HALTON MINIATURE RAILWAY

Address: Palace Fields, Town Park, Runcorn   WA7 6PT
Telephone Nº: (01928) 701965
Year Formed: 1979
Location of Line: Runcorn
Length of Line: 1 mile approximately

Nº of Steam Locos: Members locos only
Nº of Other Locos: 4
Nº of Members: Approximately 25
Annual Membership Fee: £11.00
Approx Nº of Visitors P.A.: 12,500
Gauge: 7¼ inches
Website: www.haltonminiaturerailway.co.uk

GENERAL INFORMATION

Nearest Mainline Station: Runcorn East (¾ mile)
Nearest Bus Station: Runcorn (¾ mile)
Car Parking: Available on site
Coach Parking: Available
Souvenir Shop(s): None
Food & Drinks: Available at the adjacent Ski Centre

SPECIAL INFORMATION

The railway is operated by the Halton Miniature Railway Society and one of their locomotives, the Norton Priory (illustrated above), was built by schoolchildren from Norton Priory Secondary School in 1983! It has recently been restored to its former glory and is again in regular service.

OPERATING INFORMATION

Opening Times: Sundays and Bank Holidays from April to September plus Saturdays from May to September and Thursdays in August. Trains run from 1.30pm to 4.30pm.
Steam Working: Occasional dates only. Please contact the railway for further details.
Prices: There is no charge to ride the train but donations to help cover costs are welcome.

E-mail: john@haltonminiaturerailway.co.uk

Detailed Directions by Car:
From All Parts: Exit the M56 at Junction 11 and follow the brown tourist signs for the Ski Centre which is adjacent to the railway.

HILCOTE VALLEY RAILWAY

Address: Fletchers Garden Centre, Bridge Farm, Stone Road, Eccleshall, ST21 6JY **Telephone N°**: (01785) 851057 **Year Formed**: 1993 **Location of Line**: Eccleshall, Staffordshire **Length of Line**: 500 yards	**N° of Steam Locos**: 2 **N° of Other Locos**: 2 **Approx N° of Visitors P.A.**: 5,000+ **Gauge**: 7¼ inches **Web site**: www.hilcotevalleyrailway.co.uk

GENERAL INFORMATION

Nearest Mainline Station: Stafford (6 miles)
Nearest Bus Station: Stafford (6 miles)
Car Parking: Available on site
Coach Parking: Available
Souvenir Shop(s): None
Food & Drinks: Available on site

SPECIAL INFORMATION

Railway enthusiast Roger Greatrex designed and built this railway himself!

OPERATING INFORMATION

Opening Times: Weekends and Bank Holidays from February half term until the end of October and also open during the School Holidays. Trains run from 11.00am to 4.00pm.
Steam Working: Occasional Sundays only, weather permitting.
Prices: £1.50 per ride

Detailed Directions by Car:
From All Parts: Exit the M6 at Junction 14 and take the A5013 to Eccleshall. Just after the junction with the A519, turn right onto the B5026 Stone Road and the Garden Centre is on the right at Bridge Farm after ¾ mile.

HOLLYCOMBE – STEAM IN THE COUNTRY

Address: Iron Hill, Midhurst Road, Liphook, Hants. GU30 7LP
Telephone Nº: (01428) 724900
Year Formed: 1971
Location of Line: Hollycombe, Liphook
Length of Line: 1½ miles of 2 feet gauge and a third of a mile of 7¼ inch gauge

Nº of Steam Locos: 2
Nº of Other Locos: 2
Approx Nº of Visitors P.A.: 25,000
Gauge: 2 feet and 7¼ inches
Web site: www.hollycombe.co.uk
E-mail: info@hollycombe.co.uk

GENERAL INFORMATION

Nearest Mainline Station: Liphook (1 mile)
Nearest Bus Station: Liphook
Car Parking: Extensive grass area
Coach Parking: Hardstanding
Souvenir Shop(s): Yes
Food & Drinks: Yes – Cafe

SPECIAL INFORMATION

The narrow gauge railway ascends to spectacular views of the Downs and is part of an extensive working steam museum.

OPERATING INFORMATION

Opening Times: 2019 dates: Sundays and Bank Holidays from 14th April until the 13th October. Also open from 29th May to 2nd June and daily from 30th July to 26th August (closed on Mondays in August but for 26th which is a Bank Holiday). Please check the web site for further details. Also open for a number of Special Event days. The Museum opens 11.00am to 5.00pm with rides starting at 12.30pm.
Steam Working: Please contact the museum for further information.
Prices: Adult £17.00   Senior Citizen £15.00
Child £14.00 (ages 3 to 15)
Family £55.00 (2 adults + 2 children)
Family £65.00 (2 adults + 3 children)
Disabled visitor plus a carer £17.00

Detailed Directions by Car:
Take the A3 to Liphook and follow the brown tourist signs for the museum.

Hull & District s.m.e.e.

Address: c/o 17 Orchard Close, Anlaby, Hull   HU10 6RF
Phone Nº: None
Year Formed: 1937
Location of Line: West Park, Hull
Length of Line: 190 metres (raised track) and 400 metres (ground level track)
Web site: www.finnaj.karoo.net/hdsmee.html

Nº of Steam Locos: Approximately 5
Nº of Other Locos: Approximately 10
Nº of Members: Approximately 45
Approx Nº of Visitors P.A.: 5,000
Gauge: 2½ inches, 3½ inches & 5 inches on the raised track; 5 inches & 7¼ inches on the ground level track

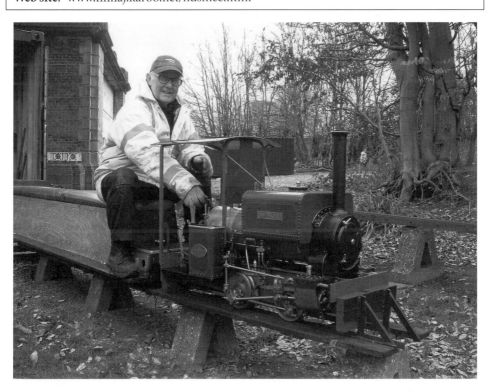

GENERAL INFORMATION

Nearest Mainline Station: Hull Paragon (1½ miles)
Nearest Bus Station: Hull Central (1½ miles)
Car Parking: Available on site
Coach Parking: None
Food & Drinks: None

SPECIAL INFORMATION

The Hull & District Society of Model & Experimental Engineers operates a railway in West Park in Hull.

OPERATING INFORMATION

Opening Times: Passenger services run on Sundays from 12.00pm until 3.00pm, Easter to October, subject to the weather and staff availability. The railway also operates on some Wednesday afternoons during the school holidays. Please contact the railway for further information.
Steam Working: Whenever available.
Prices: Train rides are 30p per person but additional donations to aid in upkeep are always welcome.

Detailed Directions by Car:
From the West, take the M62 to Hull where it becomes the A63. Continue along the A63 (Clive Sullivan Way) then turn left into Rawling Way following the signs for Hull Royal Infirmary. After ½ mile turn left onto Anlaby Road (A1105) then right after ½ mile into Walton Street. Turn right into West Park then right again for the Railway.

ICKENHAM MINIATURE RAILWAY

Correspondence: 25 Copthall Road East, Ickenham, Middlesex UB10 8SD	**N° of Steam Locos**: Up to 6
Telephone N°: (01895) 630125	**N° of Other Locos**: Up to 6
Year Formed: 1948	**N° of Members**: Approximately 60
Location: At the rear of the "Coach and Horses" Public House, Ickenham	**Approx N° of Visitors P.A.**: 9,000
	Gauge: 3½ inches and 5 inches
Length of Line: 1,100 feet	**Web site**: www.idsme.co.uk

GENERAL INFORMATION

Nearest Mainline Station: West Ruislip (½ mile)
Nearest Underground Station: Ickenham (¼ mile)
Car Parking: Public car park is adjacent
Coach Parking: None
Food & Drinks: Available

SPECIAL INFORMATION

The Railway is operated by volunteers from the Ickenham & District Society of Model Engineers.

OPERATING INFORMATION

Opening Times: The first Saturday of the month from April to December inclusive. Trains run from 12.00pm to 5.30pm (or until dusk later in the year).
Steam Working: All operating days subject to availability.
Prices: 80p per ride.

Detailed Directions by Car:
The Railway is located in Ickenham Village behind the Coach and Horses Public House which is adjacent to the junction of the B466 Ickenham High Road, B466 Long Lane and the B467 Swakeleys Road. From the East: Exit the A40 at Hillingdon Circus turning right onto the B466 Long Lane towards Ickenham/Ruislip. Continue for 1 mile and turn right into Community Close for the car park just before the Coach and Horses in the centre of Ickenham; From the West: Exit the A40 at Hillingdon Circus turning left onto B466 Long Lane. Then as above.

ILFORD & WEST ESSEX MODEL RAILWAY CLUB

Address: Station Road, Chadwell Heath, Romford, Essex RM6 4BU	**Nº of Steam Locos**: 2
Telephone Nº: (01708) 701290	**Nº of Other Locos**: 3
Year Formed: 1930	**Nº of Members**: Approximately 50
Location of Line: Chadwell Heath	**Approx Nº of Visitors P.A.**: 500
Length of Line: 150 yards	**Gauge**: 7¼ inches
	Web site: www.iwemrc.org.uk

GENERAL INFORMATION

Nearest Mainline Station: Chadwell Heath (adjacent)
Nearest Bus Station: Chadwell Heath (100 yards)
Car Parking: None on site but a public car park is 100 yards away
Coach Parking: None
Food & Drinks: Light refreshments are available

SPECIAL INFORMATION

The Ilford & West Essex Model Railway Club was formed in 1930 and as such is one of the oldest clubs of its type in the country. Please note that access to the site is by steps only and it is therefore not suitable for wheelchairs.

OPERATING INFORMATION

Opening Times: The first Sunday of the month from April to September inclusive.
Please contact the railway for further information.
Trains run from 10.30am to 4.00pm.
Steam Working: When available.
Prices: 70p per ride or £4.00 for an all-day pass

Detailed Directions by Car:
The site is alongside Chadwell Heath mainline station just off the A118 between Romford and Ilford town centres. Station Road is to the South of the A118 approximately half-way between the two towns. The site itself is approximately 200 yards down Station Road with a car park on the right hand side.

Kinver & West Midlands S.M.E.

Correspondence: Mr B. Harrison, 24 Goodrest Avenue, Halesowen B26 0HP	**Nº of Steam Locos**: 1 + Members locos
Telephone Nº: None	**Nº of Other Locos**: 2 + Members locos
Year Formed: 1961	**Nº of Members**: Approximately 100
Location of Line: Marsh Playing Fields, Kinver, Staffordshire	**Annual Membership Fee**: £52.00
	Gauge: 3½ inches and 5 inches
Length of Line: ½ mile	**Website**: www.kinvermodelengineers.org.uk
	E-mail: mike6861@blueyonder.co.uk

GENERAL INFORMATION

Nearest Mainline Station: Kidderminster (6 miles)
Nearest Bus Station: Stourbridge (3 miles)
Car Parking: Available on site
Coach Parking: Available on site
Food & Drinks: None

SPECIAL INFORMATION

The Kinver & West Midlands Society of Model Engineers dates back to organisations formed in the 1920s and has operated a railway in Kinver since 1962. In addition to the main 3½ and 5 inch line, a short 7¼ inch track is now in operation at the site.

OPERATING INFORMATION

Opening Times: Most Sunday afternoons between Easter and November, weather permitting. Trains run between 2.00pm and approximately 4.30pm. Please check the web site for further information.
Steam Working: Most operating days.
Prices: £1.00 per ride.

Detailed Directions by Car:
The Society's tracksite is situated on the Marsh Playing Fields at the end of the High Street in the village of Kinver which is to the West of Stourbridge and to the North of Kidderminster.

LANGFORD & BEELEIGH RAILWAY

Address: Museum of Power, Hatfield Road, Langford, Maldon, Essex, CM9 6QA **Telephone Nº**: (01621) 843183 **Year Formed**: 2003 **Length of Line**: ¼ mile loop	**Nº of Steam Locos**: 4 **Nº of Other Locos**: 1 **Nº of Members**: 140 (12 actively involved) **Approx Nº of Visitors P.A.**: 6,000 **Gauge**: 7¼ inches **Web site**: www.museumofpower.org.uk

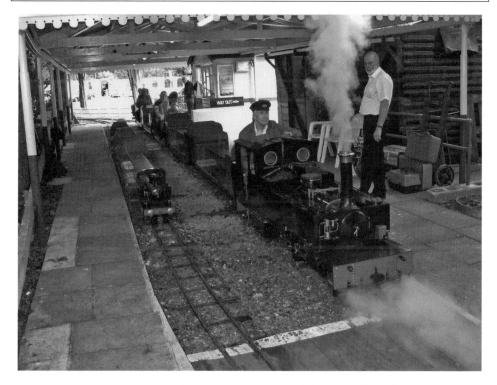

GENERAL INFORMATION

Nearest Mainline Station: Witham (4 miles)
Nearest Bus Station: Chelmsford (6 miles)
Car Parking: Available on site
Coach Parking: Available
Souvenir Shop(s): Yes
Food & Drinks: Available

SPECIAL INFORMATION

The Railway is situated at the Museum of Power which is housed in the Steam Pumping Station at Langford in Essex. The Museum was set up to exhibit and demonstrate working examples of power sources of all types and chronicle the major roles that they have played in history.

OPERATING INFORMATION

Opening Times: 2019 dates: 17th March; 21st April; 5th May; 30th June; 21st July; 4th August; 1st, 19th & 28th September; 6th October; 3rd November plus 1st December. Please contact the Museum for further information.
Steam Working: On all operating days.
Prices: £1.00 per ride (6 rides for £5.00)
Note: Admission to the Museum is an extra charge.

Detailed Directions by Car:
The Museum is situated in Langford, on the B1019 Maldon to Hatfield Peverel Road. From the A12, take the Hatfield Peverel exit, pass through the village and take the B1019 Hatfield Road towards Ulting & Maldon. The Museum is on the right hand side after approximately 3 miles on the outskirts of Langford.

LEICESTER SOCIETY OF MODEL ENGINEERS

Address: Abbey Park, Leicester LE1 3EJ	**N° of Steam Locos**: Members locos only
Telephone N°: (0116) 247-9844	**N° of Other Locos**: 6 diesels
Year Formed: 1909 (located at Abbey Park since 1951)	**N° of Members**: 100+
Location of Line: Victorian Public Park	**Annual Membership Fee**: £30.00
Length of Line: 874 yards	**Approx N° of Visitors P.A.**: 11,000
Web site: www.lsme.uk.com	**Gauges**: 2½ inches, 3½ inches, 5 inches and 7¼ inches (Also '0' and '1' gauge)

GENERAL INFORMATION

Nearest Mainline Station: Leicester (1½ miles)
Nearest Bus Station: Leicester (½ mile)
Car Parking: Available at the nearby Riverside Car Park (Pay and Display)
Coach Parking: None
Souvenir Shop(s): None
Food & Drinks: Available elsewhere in the Park

SPECIAL INFORMATION

The Society has been located within Abbey Park since 1951.

OPERATING INFORMATION

Opening Times: 2019 dates: Sundays and Bank Holidays Mondays from 31st March until 27th October. Also open on Wednesdays during the local school holidays. Santa Specials will run on 8th December – prior booking is essential.
Trains run from 1.00pm to 5.00pm
Steam Working: Subject to availability, otherwise diesel services.
Prices: Adults £1.00
Children £1.00 (Under-5s ride for free)

Detailed Directions by Car:
From All Parts: The railway is located at the South-Western edge of Leicester's Abbey Park and is best accessed from the St. Margaret's Riverside car park, situated off the A6 (North) St. Margaret's Way, adjoining the inner ring-road (Burley's Way). The station is located towards the riverside end of Cave's Walk, Abbey Park.

LITTLEDOWN MINIATURE RAILWAY

Address: Littledown Park, Chaseside, Castle Lane East, Bournemouth, BH7 7DX
Contact Telephone N⁰: 07879 355399
Year Formed: 1924
Location of Line: Littledown Park
Length of Line: Over one third of a mile

N⁰ of Steam Locos: 15+
N⁰ of Other Locos: 10+
N⁰ of Members: 140+
Approx N⁰ of Visitors P.A.: 4,000
Gauge: 3½ inches, 5 inches & 7¼ inches
Web site: www.littledownrailway.co.uk

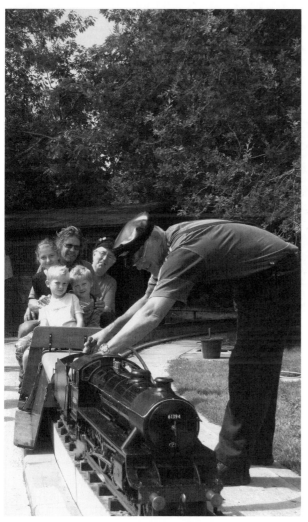

GENERAL INFORMATION

Nearest Mainline Station:
Bournemouth Central (3½ miles)
Nearest Bus Station: Bournemouth
Car Parking:
In Littledown Leisure Centre car park
Coach Parking: As above

SPECIAL INFORMATION

Bournemouth and District Society of Model Engineers operate the railway at Littledown Park. The society also operates a 16mm garden railway alongside the track.

OPERATING INFO

Opening Times: Most Sundays, Bank Holidays and Wednesdays throughout the year subject to weather conditions. Trains run from 11.00am to 3.00pm.
Steam Working: Subject to availability. Please contact the railway for further information.
Prices: £1.00 per ride.

Detailed Directions by Car:
The Railway is situated at Littledown Park which is to the North-East of Bournemouth town centre close (and to the South of) the junction of Wessex Way (A338) and Castle Lane (A3060).

LITTLE HAY MINIATURE RAILWAY

Address: Balleny Green, Little Hay Lane, Little Hay WS14 0QB	**N⁰ of Steam Locos**: 20 (approximately)
Telephone N⁰: None	**N⁰ of Other Locos**: 4
Year Formed: 1948	**N⁰ of Members**: Approximately 115
Location of Line: 100 yards from the Holly Bush Public House	**Approx N⁰ of Visitors P.A.**: 4,500
Length of Line: ½ mile (Ground level)	**Gauge**: 2½ inches, 3½ inches, 5 inches and 7¼ inches (elevated & ground level)
	Web site: www.scmes.co.uk

GENERAL INFORMATION

Nearest Mainline Station: Blake Street (1½ miles)
Nearest Bus Station: Sutton Coldfield or Lichfield (each approximately 5 miles)
Car Parking: Available on site
Coach Parking: None
Food & Drinks: Food and refreshments are available at most event and open days

SPECIAL INFORMATION

The Railway is owned and operated by members of the Sutton Coldfield Model Engineering Society Ltd. and has been based at Balleny Green since 1981. A SM32 gauge track 400 feet in length is now available and visitors can bring their own locomotives to run on it.

OPERATING INFORMATION

Opening Times: 2019 dates: 7th & 22nd April; 6th & 27th May; 2nd & 23d June; 7th July; 26th August; 6th October; 3rd November; 1st December. Santa Specials run on 14th & 15th December. Please note that rides for members of the public may not be available on all the above dates. Please check the web site for further information.
Trains generally run from 11.00am to 3.00pm.
Steam Working: All operating days.
Prices: Prices depend on the event being held.

Detailed Directions by Car:
From Lichfield: Head south on the A38 dual carriageway. Approximately ½ mile after the A38/A5 Junction, turn right at the sign for Little Hay. Follow the road past the Pumping Station and Holly Bush pub then turn left after approximately 100 yards through the steel gates set between stone pillars with lanterns to enter the railway; From the South: Heading northwards along the A38, turn left at the Little Hay sign which is located approximately 2 miles after passing the Bassets Pole Junction of the A38/A453. Then as above.

LITTLE WESTERN RAILWAY

Address: Trenance Gardens, Trenance Road, Newquay TR7 2HL	**Nº of Steam Locos:** 1
Telephone Nº: (01872) 510317	**Nº of Other Locos:** 1
Year Formed: 1965	**Approx Nº of Visitors P.A.:** Not known
Location of Line: Newquay, Cornwall	**Gauge:** 7¼ inches
Length of Line: 300 yards	**Web site:** www.lappavalley.co.uk

GENERAL INFORMATION

Nearest Mainline Station: Newquay (½ mile)
Nearest Bus Station: Newquay (½ mile)
Car Parking: Available on site
Coach Parking: Available
Souvenir Shop(s): Yes
Food & Drinks: Available

SPECIAL INFORMATION

The railway runs through the floral oasis of Trenance Gardens and close to Newquay Zoo.

OPERATING INFORMATION

Opening Times: Daily during the Summer months.
Steam Working: None at present.
Prices: Adults £1.50 (2 laps of the track)
Children £1.00 (2 laps of the track)

Detailed Directions by Car:
From All Parts: Take the A30 then the A392 to Newquay. At the roundabout turn right to continue along Trevemper Road which becomes the A3058. Turn left into Trenance Road and the gardens are a little way along.

LLWYFAN CERRIG MINIATURE RAILWAY

Address: c/o Gwili Railway, Bronwydd Arms SA33 6HT
Telephone Nº: (01267) 238213
Year Formed: 1993
Location of Line: Llwyfan Cerrig Station on the Gwili Railway
Length of Line: 300 yards

Nº of Steam Locos: None
Nº of Other Locos: 1
Nº of Members: 900 shareholders, 450 Society members (Gwili Railway)
Annual Membership Fee: £18.00
Approx Nº of Visitors P.A.: 28,000
Gauge: 7¼ inches
Web site: www.gwili-railway.co.uk

GENERAL INFORMATION

Nearest Mainline Station: Carmarthen (3 miles)
Nearest Bus Station: Carmarthen (3 miles)
Car Parking: Free parking at Bronwydd Arms
Coach Parking: Free parking at Bronwydd Arms
Souvenir Shop(s): Yes
Food & Drinks: Yes

SPECIAL INFORMATION

The railway can only be reached via the standard-gauge Gwili Railway line. The cost of rides on the miniature railway are included in the standard gauge railway fares!

OPERATING INFORMATION

Opening Times: 2019 dates: Most weekends from 13th April to the end of October and also open every Wednesday and Thursday from 17th April to the end of October. Open daily during July and August. Please phone or check the website for further details.
Steam Working: None at present
Prices: Adult £12.00   Senior Citizens £11.00
Child £6.00 (Under-3s ride for free)
Note: The above prices are for rides on the standard gauge Gwili Railway. Miniature Railway rides are included in these prices.

Detailed Directions by Car:
Gwili Railway is three miles North of Carmarthen – signposted off the A484 Carmarthen to Cardigan Road. The Llwyfan Cerrig Miniature Railway is only accessible via the Gwili Railway Line.

MOORS VALLEY RAILWAY

Address: Moors Valley Country Park, Horton Road, Ashley Heath, Nr. Ringwood, Hants. BH24 2ET	**Length of Line**: 1 mile
	Nº of Steam Locos: 15
	Nº of Other Locos: 2
Telephone Nº: (01425) 471415	**Approx Nº of Visitors P.A.**: 100,000
Year Formed: 1985	**Gauge**: 7¼ inches
Location: Moors Valley Country Park	**Web site**: www.moorsvalleyrailway.co.uk

GENERAL INFORMATION

Nearest Mainline Station: Bournemouth (12 miles)
Nearest Bus Station: Ringwood (3 miles)
Car Parking: Parking charges vary throughout the year. Maximum charge £12.00 per day.
Coach Parking: Charges are applied for parking
Souvenir Shop(s): Yes + Model Railway Shop
Food & Drinks: Yes

SPECIAL INFORMATION

The Moors Valley Railway is a complete small Railway with signalling and 2 signal boxes and also 4 tunnels and 2 level crossings.

OPERATING INFORMATION

Opening Times: 2019 dates: Weekends and school holidays throughout the year. Daily from 25th May to 2nd September and during the school holidays. Also Santa Specials in December and occasional other openings. Please phone the Railway or check the web site for details.
Steam Working: 10.45am to 5.00pm when open.
Prices: Adult Return £3.85
            Child Return £2.55
Special rates are available for parties of 10 or more and Day Rover tickets are available.

Detailed Directions by Car:
From All Parts: Moors Valley Country Park is situated on Horton Road which is off the A31 Ferndown to Ringwood road near the junction with the A338 to Bournemouth.

NATIONAL RAILWAY MUSEUM – YORK

Address: National Railway Museum, Leeman Road, York YO26 4XJ
Telephone Nº: 03330 161010
Year Formed: 1975
Location of Line: York
Length of Line: Short demonstration line

Nº of Steam Locos: 79
Nº of Other Locos: 37
Approx Nº of Visitors P.A.: 900,000
Web site: www.nrm.org.uk
E-mail: info@railwaymuseum.org.uk

GENERAL INFORMATION

Nearest Mainline Station: York (¼ mile)
Nearest Bus Station: York (¼ mile)
Car Parking: On site long stay car park
Coach Parking: On site
Souvenir Shop(s): Yes
Food & Drinks: Excellent on-site catering facilities.

SPECIAL INFORMATION

The Museum is the greatest of its kind in the world, housing the Nation's collection of locomotives, carriages, uniforms, posters and an extensive photographic archive. Special events and exhibitions run throughout the year. A 7¼ inch miniature railway offers rides in the South Yard area.

OPERATING INFORMATION

Opening Times: Open daily 10.00am to 6.00pm (or 5.00pm during the winter months). Closed from 24th to 26th of December.
Steam Working: School holidays – please phone to confirm details
Prices: Free admission but visitors are invited to make a donation. (Excludes some Special events and Steam rides). Phone 08448 153139 for details.

Detailed Directions by Car:
The Museum is located in the centre of York, just behind the Railway Station. It is clearly signposted from all approaches to York.

NESS ISLANDS RAILWAY

Address: Whin Park, Inverness IV3 5SS	**Nº of Steam Locos**: 1
Telephone Nº: (01463) 235533	**Nº of Other Locos**: 1
Year Formed: 1983	**Approx Nº of Visitors P.A.**: 12,000
Location of Line: Inverness	**Gauge**: 7¼ inches
Length of Line: 900 yards	**Web site**: www.nessislandsrailway.co.uk

GENERAL INFORMATION

Nearest Mainline Station: Inverness (2 miles)
Nearest Bus Station: Inverness (2 miles)
Car Parking: Available on site
Coach Parking: Available
Souvenir Shop(s): Yes
Food & Drinks: None

SPECIAL INFORMATION

Ness Islands Railway is Britain's most northerly 7¼ inch gauge line.

OPERATING INFORMATION

Opening Times: 2019 dates: Weekends from Easter to the end of October and also daily during the school holidays.
Trains run from 11.30am to 4.30pm.
Steam Working: Most weekends.
Prices: £2.50 per ride (Under-4s ride for free)

Detailed Directions by Car:
From All Parts: The Railway is located in Inverness, just to the south of the A82 Glenurquhart Road. Turn into Bught Road at Queens Park and the railway is on the right after a short distance.

NORTH SCARLE MINIATURE RAILWAY

Address: North Scarle Playing Field, Swinderby Road, North Scarle, Lincolnshire LN6 9ER (for SatNav)
Telephone Nº: (01427) 881698
Year Formed: 1933
Location of Line: North Scarle, between Newark and Lincoln
Length of Line: A third of a mile

Nº of Steam Locos: 7
Nº of Other Locos: 8
Nº of Members: 52
Annual Membership Fee: See web site
Approx Nº of Visitors P.A.: 3,000
Gauges: 7¼ inches and 5 inches
Web site: www.lincolnmes.co.uk

GENERAL INFORMATION

Nearest Mainline Station: Newark Northgate (5 miles)
Nearest Bus Station: Newark (5 miles)
Car Parking: 300 spaces available on site
Coach Parking: None available
Souvenir Shop(s): None
Food & Drinks: Available on special days only

SPECIAL INFORMATION

The Railway is owned and operated by the Lincoln and District Model Engineering Society which was founded in 1933.

OPERATING INFORMATION

Opening Times: Car Boot Sale Sundays only!
Dates for 2019: 31st March; 14th & 28th April; 12th & 26th May; 9th & 23rd June; 7th & 21st July; 4th & 18th August; 1st & 15th September.
Trains run from 9.00am to 12.00pm.
An open weekend is to be held on 21st & 22nd September.
Steam Working: Every running day.
Prices: Adult Return £1.00
Child Return £1.00

Detailed Directions by Car:
North Scarle is situated off the A46 between Lincoln and Newark (about 5 miles from Newark). Alternatively, take the A1133 from Gainsborough and follow the North Scarle signs when around 6 miles from Newark.

NORTHAMPTON SOCIETY OF MODEL ENGINEERS

Contact Address: 7 Hodnet Close,
Northampton   NN4 0XY
Telephone Nº: 0790 705-1388
Year Formed: 1933
Location of Line: Lower Delapre Park,
London Road, Northampton   NN4 8AJ
Length of Line: 1,740 feet (raised track)
and 3,034 feet (ground level track)

Nº of Steam Locos: Up to 9 running
Nº of Other Locos: 4 to 6 run occasionally
Nº of Members: 145
Approx Nº of Visitors P.A.: 10,000
Gauge: 3½ inches, 5 inches & 7¼ inches
Web site: www.nsme.co.uk

GENERAL INFORMATION

Nearest Mainline Station: Northampton (2 miles)
Nearest Bus Station: Northampton (2 miles)
Car Parking: Available on site
Coach Parking: On London Road
Food & Drinks: Light refreshments are available

SPECIAL INFORMATION

The Northampton Society of Model Engineers is a
long established society with excellent facilities for
model engineers. The society has over 140 members
with wide ranging interests, several of whom have
won major awards at National exhibitions.

The two tracks were extended during 2011 and are
located in a woodland setting with a new garden
railway and a picnic site. The site may be hired for
Birthday parties on Tuesdays and Saturdays.
Please check the web site for further information.

OPERATING INFORMATION

Opening Times: May Day Bank Holiday Monday
then the first Sunday of the month thereafter up to
and including October. Trains run from 2.00pm to
5.00pm.
Steam Working: Every operating day.
Prices: £1.00 per ride

Detailed Directions by Car:
From the M1: Exit at Junction 15 and take the A508 to Northampton. Take the 2nd turn off onto the A45 (for the
Town Centre) and then the 2nd exit at the roundabout. After ½ mile turn right just before the pelican crossing
and immediately turn left through the steel gate onto the access track for the railway; From the East: Follow the
A45 and take the turn off signposted for Daventry and the Town Centre. Take the 4th exit at the roundabout onto
the A508, then as above; From the Town Centre: Take the A508 South (Bridge Street). Cross the river and go
straight on at the traffic lights. Pass a petrol station on the left and immediately after the pelican crossing turn left
then immediately left again for the railway.

NORWICH & DISTRICT S.M.E.

Address: Eaton Park, Colman Road, Norwich NR4 7AU
Telephone Nº: None
Year Formed: 1933
Location of Line: Eaton Park, Norwich
Length of Line: Two tracks – 'Mainline' is 800 metres (7¼ and 5 inch gauges) and the 'Heritage Track' is 955 feet (raised 5 and 3½ inch gauges)

Nº of Steam Locos: 2 + visiting locos
Nº of Other Locos: 2
Nº of Members: Approximately 110
Approx Nº of Visitors P.A.: 16,000
Gauge: 3½ inches, 5 inches & 7¼ inches
Web site: www.ndsme.org
E-mail: epmrinfo@ndsme.org
Facebook: 'Eaton Park Miniature Railway'

GENERAL INFORMATION

Nearest Mainline Station: Norwich (3 miles)
Nearest Bus Station: Norwich (2 miles)
Car Parking: Available in Eaton Park
Coach Parking: None
Food & Drinks: Available in Eaton Park

SPECIAL INFORMATION

Norwich & District Society of Model Engineers was formed in 1933 and operates two tracks in Eaton Park. The 'Mainline' is a 7¼ inch and 5 inch ground level track and the 'Heritage Track' is a raised tracking using 5 inch and 3½ inch gauges.

OPERATING INFORMATION

Opening Times: 2019 dates: Sundays and Bank Holidays from 7th April to 6th October. Trains run from 1.00pm to 5.00pm, weather permitting.
Steam Working: Most operating days
Prices: £1.00 per ride on the 'Mainline'
50p per ride on the 'Heritage Track'

Detailed Directions by Car:
Take the A11 or A140 into Norwich and upon reaching the ring road, turn left. At the second set of traffic lights turn left into South Park Avenue and the entrance to Eaton Park is on the right hand side.
Alternative route: Take the A47 into Norwich and turn right at the ring road. At the 3rd set of traffic lights turn right into South Park Avenue.

PICNIC FIELD RAILWAY

Correspondence: c/o 21 Talisman Street, Hitchin   SG4 0EZ
Telephone Nº: 07758 121338
Year Formed: 1980
Location: Audley End Miniature Railway
Length of Line: 1,300 feet
Nº of Steam Locos: Several members' locos

Nº of Other Locos: 2 + members' locos
Nº of Members: 60
Approx Nº of Visitors P.A.: 12,000
Gauge: 5 inches and 7¼ inches
Web site: None at present
E-mail: events@westonstar.org.uk

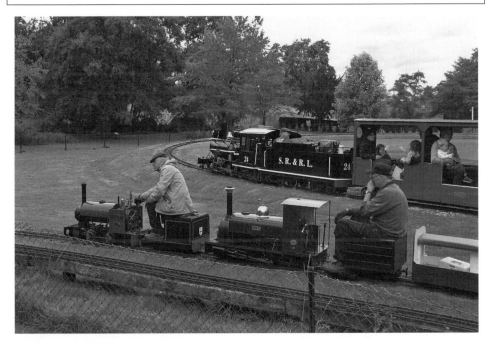

GENERAL INFORMATION

Nearest Mainline Station: Audley End (1 mile)
Nearest Bus Station: Saffron Walden (1 mile)
Car Parking: On site plus further overflow parking
Coach Parking: Available by prior arrangement with the Audley End Railway
Souvenir Shop(s): Yes – at the Audley End Railway
Food & Drinks: Yes – at the Audley End Railway

SPECIAL INFORMATION

The Saffron Walden & District Society of Model Engineers operates the "Picnic Field Railway" in the grounds of the 10¼ inch Audley End Steam Railway, opposite Audley End House. Visitors are required to buy an Audley End Railway admission ticket for access to the site.

OPERATING INFORMATION

Opening Times: Most weekends when the Audley End Railway is open, from Easter to October and on selected other dates.
Steam Working: Various dates throughout the year.
Prices: £1.00 per ride (A Multi-ride ticket is £3.00)
Note: Visitors need to buy an Audley End Railway admission ticket for access to the site.

Detailed Directions by Car:
Exit the M11 at Junction 10 if southbound or Junction 9 if northbound and follow the signs for Audley End House. The railway is situated just across the road from Audley End House.

PINEWOOD MINIATURE RAILWAY

Address: Pinewood Leisure Centre, Old Wokingham Road, Wokingham, Berkshire RG40 3AQ
Phone Nº: None
Year Formed: 1984
Location: Pinewood Leisure Centre
Length of Line: 800 metres

Nº of Steam Locos: 17 (All owned
Nº of Other Locos: 10 by Members)
Nº of Members: Approximately 40
Annual Membership Fee: £50.00
Approx Nº of Visitors P.A.: 3,000
Gauge: 5 inches and 7¼ inches
Web site: www.pinewoodrailway.co.uk

GENERAL INFORMATION

Nearest Mainline Station: Bracknell
Nearest Bus Station: Bracknell
Car Parking: Available on site
Coach Parking: Available by arrangement
Souvenir Shop(s): None
Food & Drinks: Light refreshments are available

SPECIAL INFORMATION

The Pinewood Miniature Railway runs through attractive woodlands backing on to a Leisure Centre.

OPERATING INFORMATION

Opening Times: 2019 dates: Public running on the 3rd Sunday in the month from March to October. Santa Specials on the first two Sundays in December (pre-booking is required for these dates). Private Parties can sometimes be catered for by prior arrangement. Trains run from 1.30pm to 4.00pm.
Steam Working: All open days.
Prices: £1.00 per ride or 6 rides for £5.00
Note: Under-3s ride free of charge

Detailed Directions by Car:
From the M3 or the A30 take the A322 towards Bracknell. Once on the A322, keep in the left hand lane to the first major roundabout then take the first exit onto the B3430 towards Wokingham along Nine Mile Ride. Cross the next roundabout (A3095) and continue on the B3430 passing the Golden Retriever pub and the Crematorium. Go straight on at the next mini-roundabout then turn right at the following roundabout into Old Wokingham Road. The Pinewood Leisure Centre is on the left after approximately 100 metres.

PLYMOUTH MINIATURE STEAM

Address: Goodwin Park, Pendeen Crescent, Southway, Plymouth PL6 6RE **Phone No**: (01752) 661780 (Secretary) **Year Formed**: 1970 **Location of Line**: Goodwin Park Public Nature Reserve **Length of Line**: ½ mile	**No of Steam Locos**: 2 + member locos **No of Other Locos**: 2 + member locos **No of Members**: Approximately 100 **Approx No of Visitors P.A.**: 2,000 **Gauge**: 3½ inches, 5 inches & 7¼ inches **Web site**: www.plymouthminiaturesteam.co.uk

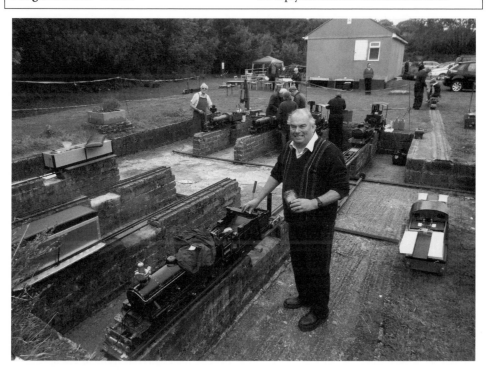

GENERAL INFORMATION

Nearest Mainline Station: Plymouth (6 miles)
Nearest Bus Station: Plymouth (6 miles)
Car Parking: Available on site (limited headroom)
Coach Parking: None
Food & Drinks: Light refreshments available.

SPECIAL INFORMATION

The railway runs through Goodwin Park, a site specially developed by members of the Society which was opened in 1990 and has since been designated as a Public Nature Reserve.

OPERATING INFORMATION

Opening Times: Open during the 1st and 3rd Sunday afternoons of each month from April to October inclusive, from 2.00pm to 4.30pm.
Steam Working: Most operating days.
Prices: 90p per ride.

Detailed Directions by Car:
From the A38 Plymouth Parkway, follow the signs for Tavistock (A386) travelling North until reaching a new road junction near Plymouth Airport and a Park & Ride site. Turn left at this junction into the Southway Estate and follow the road for ½ mile past two mini-roundabouts and a set of traffic lights. At the 3rd mini-roundabout turn left into Pendeen Crescent and about 200 yard on the right is a signpost for the railway. Follow the lane to the parking area but please note that the bridge has just 6 feet headroom so large vehicles must park outside the track!

POPLAR MINIATURE RAILWAY

Address: Poplar Nurseries, Coggleshall Road, Marks Tey, Near Colchester, CO6 1HR
Telephone Nº: 07780 603001
Year Formed: 2013
Location: Poplar Garden Centre

Length of Line: 350 yards
Nº of Steam Locos: 2
Nº of Other Locos: 1
Approx Nº of Visitors P.A.: 49,000
Gauge: 7¼ inches
Web site: www.poplarminirail.co.uk

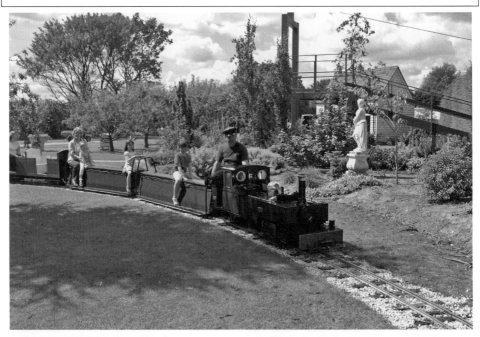

GENERAL INFORMATION

Nearest Mainline Station: Marks Tey (1½ miles)
Nearest Bus Station: Colchester (8 miles) – Service 70 from Colchester to Braintree runs past the site.
Car Parking: Available on site
Coach Parking: Available on site
Souvenir Shop(s): Available
Food & Drinks: Restaurant available on site

SPECIAL INFORMATION

The Railway runs through the gardens of Poplar Nurseries and complements the other attractions of the garden centre which include a restaurant, farm shop and play area.

E-mail: info@poplarrailway.co.uk

OPERATING INFORMATION

Opening Times: 2019 dates: Weekends and Bank Holidays from 16th February to the end of December (but closed on 21st April). Open daily from 22nd April to the 2nd September and also for special Halloween and Christmas events in October and December respectively. Please contact the railway for details about these Special Events. Trains run from 10.30am to 4.00pm except for most weekdays from April to the end of July when they run from 10.00am to 2.00pm.
Steam Working: Most operating days.
Prices: £2.00 per person for the first ride then £1.00 for each additional ride that day. Under-4s travel free of charge but must be accompanied by an adult. Special Travel Cards offering 10 or 20 rides for regular visitors are available.

Detailed Directions by Car:
From the M11, Stansted and the North: Exit the M11 at Junction 8 and follow the A120 to Marks Tey. Poplar Nurseries is situated on the right hand side of the road; From London and the South: Take the A12 for Colchester then turn off onto the A120 at Junction 25. Follow the A120 and Stansted Airport signs for 1 mile from the junction and Poplar Nurseries is located on the left hand side of the road.

PORTERSWICK JUNCTION LIGHT RAILWAY

Address: Hidden Valley Discovery Park, Tredidon St. Thomas, Launceston, Cornwall   PL15 8SJ
Telephone Nº: (01566) 86463
Year Formed: 2003
Location of Line: Near Launceston
Length of Line: 1 mile

Nº of Steam Locos: None
Nº of Other Locos: 1
Approx Nº of Visitors P.A.: 26,000
Gauge: 7¼ inches
Web site:
www.hiddenvalleydiscoverypark.co.uk

GENERAL INFORMATION

Nearest Mainline Station: Liskeard (16 miles)
Nearest Bus Station: Launceston (4 miles)
Car Parking: Available on site
Coach Parking: Available on site
Souvenir Shop(s): Yes
Food & Drinks: Available

SPECIAL INFORMATION

The railway is situated in the grounds of Hidden Valley Discovery Park which also contains a number of other attractions including various trails, a mystery mansion, gardens and, during 2019, a new attraction: Tibbohton.

OPERATING INFORMATION

Opening Times: 2019 dates: Daily from 6th April to 22nd September and also from 19th to 27th October. Open from 10.00am to 5.00pm with the last admission at 2.00pm each day.
Steam Working: None at present.
Prices: Adult £11.50
　　　　　　Child £10.50 (Free for ages 3 and under)
　　　　　　Concession £9.50
Note: The above prices are for entry into the Park which includes the cost of train rides.

Detailed Directions by Car:
Take the A30 from Exeter towards Bodmin and then (shortly after Launceston) take the A395 towards Davidstow and Bude. After about one mile, turn right following the brown tourist signs for 'Hidden Valley'. The railway is located in the Discovery Park approximately ¾ mile along this road.

PORTHMADOG WOODLAND RAILWAY

Address: Tremadog Road, Porthmadog, Gwynedd LL49 9DY	**Nº of Steam Locos**: 5
Telephone Nº: (01766) 513402	**Nº of Other Locos**: 19
Year Formed: 1961	**Nº of Members**: 1,000
Location of Line: At the Welsh Highland Heritage Railway	**Annual Membership Fee**: £30.00 Adult
	Approx Nº of Visitors P.A.: 25,000
Length of Line: 550 yards	**Gauge**: 7¼ inches
	Web site: www.whr.co.uk

GENERAL INFORMATION

Nearest Mainline Station: Porthmadog (adjacent)
Nearest Bus Station: Services 1 & 3 stop 50 yards away
Car Parking: Free parking at site, plus a public Pay and Display car park within 100 yards
Coach Parking: Adjacent
Souvenir Shop(s): Yes – large range available
Food & Drinks: Yes – excellent home cooking at the Russell Team Room!

SPECIAL INFORMATION

The Porthmadog Woodland Railway is located at the Welsh Highland Heritage Railway. Tickets for the WHHR entitle customers to free rides on the Woodland Railway.

OPERATING INFORMATION

Opening Times: 2019 dates: Daily from 4th May to 2nd November except for most Mondays and Fridays in May, June, September and October. Also open daily during local school holidays and at weekends during April. Trains run from 10.30am to 4.00pm.
Steam Working: Most days during the School Holidays and on other selected weekends. Please check with the railway for further details.
Prices: Adult Day Rover £9.50
Child Day Rover £4.75 (Under-3s free)
Family Day Rover £25.00
(2 adults + 2 children)

Detailed Directions by Car:
From Bangor/Caernarfon take the A487 to Porthmadog. From Pwllheli take the A497 to Porthmadog then turn left at the roundabout. From the Midlands take A487 to Portmadog. Once in Porthmadog, follow the brown tourist signs. The line is located right next to Porthmadog Mainline Station, opposite the Queens Hotel.

PUGNEYS LIGHT RAILWAY

Address: Pugneys Country Park, Denby Dale Road, Wakefield WF2 7EQ	**Nº of Steam Locos**: 2
Telephone Nº: 07885 930523	**Nº of Other Locos**: 6 at present
Year Formed: 1998	**Approx Nº of Visitors P.A.**: 16,000
Location of Line: Pugneys Country Park	**Gauge**: 7¼ inches
Length of Line: 1,400 yards	**facebook**: PugneysLightRailway

GENERAL INFORMATION

Nearest Mainline Station: Wakefield (1½ miles)
Nearest Bus Station: Wakefield (2 miles)
Car Parking: Available on site
Coach Parking: Available by prior arrangement
Souvenir Shop(s): Yes
Food & Drinks: Available

SPECIAL INFORMATION

The railway is steadily improving and developing and is operated by a dedicated group of volunteers. The line runs part way around one of two lakes in Pugneys Country Park, once an open cast mine and gravel quarry, and the journey offers extensive views of Sandal Castle across the main lake. Bike hire, a café, footpaths/cycle paths around the main lake and a children's play area can also be found in the Park.

OPERATING INFORMATION

Opening Times: Weekends and Bank Holidays throughout the year and also during the School Holidays. Open other days by special arrangement. Opening days are weather-dependent so please phone or check the Facebook page before visiting. Open 11.00am to 4.00pm (until 5.00pm during British Summer Time) and often later during Special Events.
Steam Working: Most Sundays plus some Saturdays during the summer months. Visiting locos occasionally operate on the line.
Prices: £2.00 per return journey
£1.00 per single journey
Note: Visiting locos are welcome by prior arrangement and Special events can be booked by prior arrangement.

Detailed Directions by Car:
From All Parts: Exit the M1 at Junction 39 and take the A636 towards Wakefield. After approximately 1 mile, turn right at the 2nd roundabout into the Park.

RAINSBROOK VALLEY RAILWAY

Address: Rugby Model Engineering
Society, Onley Lane, Rugby CV22 5QD
Telephone Nº: None
Year Formed: 1949
Location of Line: Onley Lane, Rugby
Length of Line: 1,770 yards ground level
(7¼ inch) and also 1,100 feet elevated
(2½, 3½ & 5 inch gauges)

Nº of Steam Locos: 10
Nº of Other Locos: 4+
Nº of Members: 90
Annual Membership Fee: £45.00
Approx Nº of Visitors P.A.: 6,000
Gauges: 2½ inches, 3½ inches, 5 inches &
7¼ inches
Web site: www.rugbymes.co.uk

GENERAL INFORMATION

Nearest Mainline Station: Rugby (2½ miles)
Nearest Bus Station: Rugby (2½ miles)
Car Parking: Available on site
Coach Parking: None
Souvenir Shop(s): None
Food & Drinks: Light refreshments only

SPECIAL INFORMATION

The Rainsbrook Valley Railway is operated by
members of the Rugby Model Engineering Society Ltd.

OPERATING INFORMATION

Opening Times: 2019 dates: 28th April; 19th May;
20th & 21st July (for a special event celebrating the
70th Anniversary of the railway, during which a new
station will open); 18th August; 15th September;
20th October and 22nd December.
Trains run from 2.00pm to 5.00pm (3.00pm to
6.00pm in December).
Steam Working: All operating days
Prices: £1.50 a ride (Under-3s free of charge)

Detailed Directions by Car:
From the M1: Exit at Junction 18 and follow the A428 westwards towards Rugby. After 3 miles turn left on to the
B4429 towards Dunchurch. After 1 mile turn left at the crossroads into Onley Lane and the Railway is on the right
hand side after 300 yards; From Dunchurch: Follow the A426 Northwards then turn onto the B4429 at the
roundabout travelling Eastwards. After 1 mile turn right at the crossroads into Onley Lane for the Railway; From
Rugby: In Rugby, follow signs for the Hospital in Barby Road then continue South for 1 mile. At the crossroads
go straight on over the B4429 into Onley Lane for the Railway.

READING SOCIETY OF MODEL ENGINEERS

Address: Prospect Park, 82 Bath Road, Reading, Berkshire   RG30 2BJ
Telephone Nº: 07881 960445
Year Formed: 1909 (line since 1975)
Location of Line: Prospect Park, Reading
Length of Line: Two lines, one of 1,100 feet and one of 1,350 feet

Nº of Steam Locos: 2 + members locos
Nº of Other Locos: 5 + members locos
Nº of Members: Approximately 120
Annual Membership Fee: £42.00
Approx Nº of Visitors P.A.: 25,000
Gauge: 2½ inches, 3½ inches, 5 inches and 7¼ inches

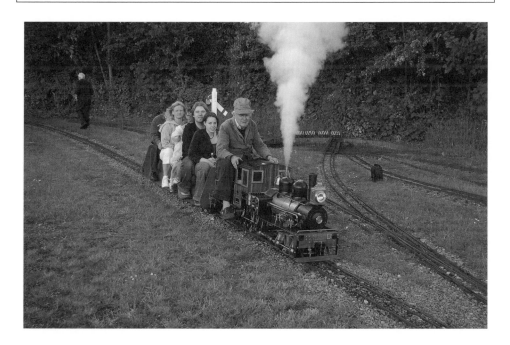

GENERAL INFORMATION

Nearest Mainline Station: Reading (2 miles)
Nearest Bus Station: Reading Station (2 miles)
Car Parking: Available on site
Coach Parking: Available by prior arrangement
Souvenir Shop(s): None
Food & Drinks: Available

SPECIAL INFORMATION

The Reading SME has been using the current site for more than 40 years and it now boasts a well equipped club house and useful workshop facilities.

To find the railway on facebook, search for 'Prospect Park Railway - Reading Society of Model Engineers'.

OPERATING INFORMATION

Opening Times: The first Sunday of the month throughout the year and also some Bank Holidays. Please check the facebook page for further details. Trains run from 1.00pm to 4.30pm (times vary during the Winter months).
Steam Working: All operating days
Prices: 60p per ride or 10 rides for £5.00

Detailed Directions by Car:
Exit the M4 at Junction 12 and take the A4 Bath Road towards Reading. Continue on this road for approximately 2¼ miles. Prospect Park is on the left, continue along Bath Road almost to the end of Prospect Park and the entrance to the car park for the railway is on the left about 100 metres before the traffic lights.

ROXBOURNE PARK MINIATURE RAILWAY

Address: Roxbourne Park, Field End Road, Eastcote, Ruislip HA4 9PB **Telephone Nº:** None **E-mail:** info@hwsme.org **Year Formed:** 1936 **Location of Line:** Roxbourne Park **Length of Line:** 2,200 feet	**Nº of Steam Locos:** Members locos only **Nº of Other Locos:** Members locos only **Nº of Members:** Approximately 128 **Annual Membership Fee:** £25.00 (Adult) **Approx Nº of Visitors P.A.:** 2,500 **Gauge:** 3½ inches, 5 inches & 7¼ inches **Web site:** www.hwsme.org

GENERAL INFORMATION

Nearest Tube Station: Eastcote (½ mile)
Nearest Bus Station: –
Car Parking: Free parking is available on site
Coach Parking: None
Food & Drinks: None

SPECIAL INFORMATION

The railway is operated by members of the Harrow & Wembley Society of Model Engineers which has been running passenger services on the current track in Roxbourne Park since 1979.

OPERATING INFORMATION

Opening Times: 2019 dates: Every Sunday from 31st March to 20th October inclusive with trains running from 2.30pm to 5.00pm. A special Halloween train runs on 27th October from 1.00pm to 4.00pm and Father Christmas trains operate on 8th December during the same hours.
For details of further special events, please check the society's web site.
Steam Working: Every operating day.
Prices: £1.00 per ride

Detailed Directions by Car:
Exit the M40 at Target roundabout and travel into Northolt Village on the A312. Turn left into Eastcote Lane North after the traffic lights just after Northolt Station and continue along this road. Eastcote Lane becomes Field End Road and Roxbourne Park is a little further on opposite Venue '5' (formerly The Clay Pigeon Public House).

ROYDS PARK MINIATURE RAILWAY

Year Formed: 1950 **Location**: Royds Park, Cleckheaton, BD19 5LL **Telephone Nº**: 07928 337668 **Length of Line**: One tenth of a mile	**Nº of Steam Locos**: 3 (+ members locos) **Nº of Other Locos**: 2 (+ members locos) **Nº of Members**: 24 **Approx Nº of Visitors P.A.**: 3,000 **Gauge**: 5 inches and 7¼ inches **Web site**: www.roydsparkrailway.co.uk

GENERAL INFORMATION

Nearest Mainline Station: Dewsbury (5 miles)
Nearest Bus Station: Cleckheaton
Car Parking: Approximately 20 spaces on site
Coach Parking: None
Food & Drinks: Light refreshments available

SPECIAL INFORMATION

Spenborough Model & Experimental Engineers operate their service on two tracks in Royds Park which are built on the trackbed of the old London & North West Railway. The club operates a Cromar white carriage for wheelchair passengers.

OPERATING INFORMATION

Opening Times: 2019 dates: Every 2nd and 4th Sunday from 24th March to 3rd November and also Wednesdays during the summer school holidays. Trains run from 1.00pm to 4.00pm on these dates. Mince Pie Specials run on 15th December from 1.00pm to 4.00pm.
Please check the web site for further information.
Steam Working: Most operating days.
Prices: £1.00 per ride (3 circuits of the track).

Detailed Directions by Car:
Exit the M62 at Junction 26 and turn off at the roundabout onto the A638 Cleckheaton to Dewsbury road. Travel through Cleckheaton for approximately ¾ mile then, just after the start of the dual carriageway, turn left onto New Street and at the top of the street is the entrance to Royds Park.

RYEDALE SOCIETY OF MODEL ENGINEERS

Address: The Club House, Pottergate, Gilling East, North Yorkshire   YO62 4JJ
Telephone Nº: None
Year Formed: 1983
Location of Line: Gilling East
Length of Line: 450 metres

Nº of Steam Locos: 10
Nº of Other Locos: Several
Nº of Members: 60
Annual Membership Fee: £75.00
Approx Nº of Visitors P.A.: 3,500
Gauge: 3½ inches, 5 inches and 7¼ inches
Web site: www.rsme.org.uk

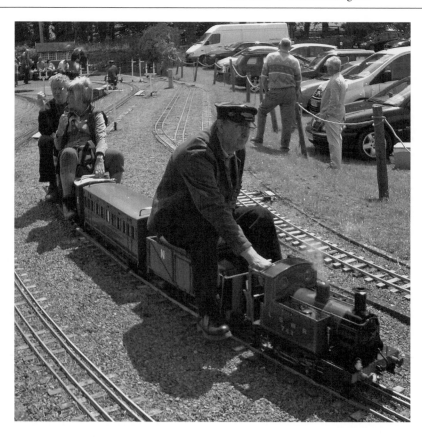

GENERAL INFORMATION

Nearest Mainline Station: Thirsk (11 miles)
Nearest Bus Station: Helmsley (5 miles)
Car Parking: Available on site
Coach Parking: Available
Souvenir Shop(s): None
Food & Drinks: Available

OPERATING INFORMATION

Opening Times: 2019 dates: Easter Sunday then every Sunday to 29th September except for 19th May, 2nd June and 25th August which are special event days for spectators only (no rides available). Open from 12.30pm to 4.30pm.
Steam Working: Every operating day.
Prices: £1.00 per ride

Detailed Directions by Car:
Gilling East is situated approximately 3 miles south of Helmsley (which is on the A170 Thirsk to Scarborough road). Gilling East is on the B1363 which joins the B1257 at nearby Oswaldkirk. Head West at the crossroads by the Fairfax Arms, signposted for the Golf Club and The Old School is situated on the right after around 200 yards.

SCOTTISH MODEL ENGINEERING TRUST

Address: Wester Pickston Railway, College Road, Glenalmond PH1 3RX
Telephone Nº: (01764) 653660
Year Formed: 2003
Location: Glenalmond, near Perth
Length of Line: 2,000 metres (2,187 yards)

Nº of Steam Locos: Members' locos only
Nº of Other Locos: Members' locos only
Nº of Members: Approximately 90
Annual Membership Fee: See web site
Approx Nº of Visitors P.A.: 7,500
Gauges: 5 inches and 7¼ inches
Web site: www.smet.org.uk

GENERAL INFORMATION

Nearest Mainline Station: Perth (10 miles)
Nearest Bus Station: Perth (10 miles)
Car Parking: Free parking is available on site
Coach Parking: Available by prior arrangement
Souvenir Shop(s): None
Food & Drinks: Available

SPECIAL INFORMATION

The Trust was formed in 2001 out of the Perth Society of Model and Experimental Engineers which started in 1935. The aim of the Trust is to demonstrate Scotland's engineering heritage through exhibitions, lectures and the sharing of the hobby in general.

OPERATING INFORMATION

Opening Times: 2019 dates: 21st April (Easter Sunday); 26th May; 4th and 25th August.
Open from 11.30am to 4.00pm on these days. In addition, there are always members up at the track every Thursday & Sunday and visitors are welcome.
Steam Working: All open days.
Prices: £2.00 per ride or 6 rides for £10.00

Detailed Directions by Car:
From All Parts: Take the A85 from Perth to Methven and turn right onto College Road opposite the Post Office. The railway is 3 miles to the north of Methven on the right-hand side of the road.

STANSTED PARK LIGHT RAILWAY

Address: Stansted House, Rowlands Castle PO9 6DX	**N° of Steam Locos:** 4
Telephone N°: (023) 9241-3324	**N° of Other Locos:** 3
Year Formed: 2005	**Approx N° of Visitors P.A.:** 20,000
Location: Stansted House, Hampshire	**Gauge:** 7¼ inches
Length of Line: ½ mile	
Web site: www.stanstedpark.co.uk/visitor-attractions/stansted-light-railway.html	

GENERAL INFORMATION

Nearest Mainline Station: Rowlands Castle (1¼ miles)
Nearest Bus Station: Hilsea Portsmouth (5 miles)
Car Parking: Available on site
Coach Parking: Available
Souvenir Shop(s): At the Garden Centre
Food & Drinks: Available

SPECIAL INFORMATION

The railway is located within the grounds of Stansted House which stands in 1,800 acres of ancient forest on the South Downs. The line passes through the Bessborough Arboretum.

OPERATING INFORMATION

Opening Times: Wednesdays, weekends and Bank Holidays throughout the year and daily during the School Holidays. Trains run from 11.00am to 4.00pm.
Steam Working: Most opening days during the Summer, weather permitting.
Prices: Adults £2.00
Children £1.50 (Free for Under-2s)
Concessions £1.50

Detailed Directions by Car:
From All Parts: Exit the A3(M) at Junction 2 and take the B2149 towards Rowlands Castle.

STOKE PARK RAILWAY

Address: Burchatts Farm, Stoke Park, Guildford, Surrey GU1 1TU
Telephone Nº: None
Year Formed: 1954
Location of Line: Stoke Park, Guildford
Length of Line: 990 feet ground level track and 1,405 feet raised track

Nº of Steam Locos: 6 + visiting locos
Nº of Other Locos: 2
Nº of Members: Over 200
Approx Nº of Visitors P.A.: 10,000
Gauges: 7¼ inches, 5 inches, 3½ inches and 2½ inches
Web site: www.gmes.org.uk
E-mail: pr@gmes.org.uk

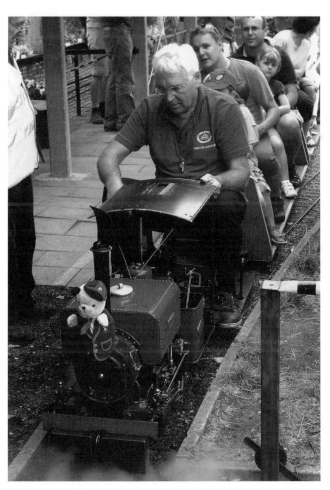

GENERAL INFO

Nearest Mainline Station:
Guildford London Road (½ mile)
Nearest Bus Station:
Guildford (2½ miles)
Car Parking: Street parking + some available on site
Coach Parking:
Street parking only
Souvenir Shop(s): None
Food & Drinks: Available

SPECIAL INFO

The Guildford Model Engineering Society has operated a miniature railway at the Burchatts Farm site since 1958 and now also has two Garden railways operating on the site.

OPERATING INFO

Opening Times:
2019 Dates: 17th March; 14th April; 19th May; 23rd June; 28th July; 18th August; 15th September and 20th October – open from 2.00pm to 5.00pm on these dates. Also open for the Stoke Park Railway Gala weekend on 6th & 7th July from 10.00am to 5.00pm and a Christmas Special operates on 8th December, 11.00am to 3.00pm.
Steam Working: Every open day.
Prices: 1 ride for £1.50
              5 rides for £5.00

Detailed Directions by Car:
The Railway is located at the Eastern end of Stoke Park in Guildford, not far from the Spectrum Sports Centre and near to the junction of the A25 (Parkway) and the A3100 (London Road). Access to the Burchatts Farm site is via London Road.

STRAND MINIATURE RAILWAY

Address: Strand Leisure Park, Pier Approach, Gillingham ME7 1TT	**Nº of Steam Locos:** None
Telephone Nº: (01634) 333927	**Nº of Other Locos:** 1
Year Formed: 1948	**Approx Nº of Visitors P.A.:** Not known
Location of Line: Strand Leisure Park	**Gauge:** 7¼ inches
	Length of Line: 400 yards (circular)

GENERAL INFORMATION

Nearest Mainline Station: Gillingham (1 mile)
Nearest Bus Station: Gillingham (1 mile)
Car Parking: Available at the Leisure Park
Coach Parking: None
Souvenir Shop(s): None
Food & Drinks: Cafeteria at the park

SPECIAL INFORMATION

The railway is located within The Strand Leisure Park, one of Medway's most popular leisure attractions.

OPERATING INFORMATION

Opening Times: 2019 dates: Weekends and Bank Holidays from April to September. Trains run from 11.00am to 5.00pm.
Steam Working: None
Prices: £1.00 a ride (two laps of the track)

Detailed Directions by Car:

Strand Miniature Railway is located within The Strand Leisure Park on the banks of the River Medway in Gillingham. Exit the A2/M2 onto the A289 and follow the road into Gillingham, crossing the bridge over the River Medway into Pier Road. Pass the University of Greenwich Medway campus on the right and continue along Pier Road, passing Liberty Quays before turning left at the roundabout for The Strand.

STRATHAVEN MINIATURE RAILWAY

Address: George Allan Park, Threestanes Road, Strathaven ML10 6EF
Telephone Nº: (01357) 521995
Year Formed: 1949
Location of Line: George Allan Park
Length of Line: 2,270 feet of 5 inch and 7¼ inch gauge on the ground level track. The raised track of 2½ inch, 3½ inch and 5 inch gauges is 408 feet in length

Nº of Steam Locos: 2 (+ Members locos)
Nº of Other Locos: 3
Nº of Members: Approximately 30
Approx Nº of Visitors P.A.: 12,000
Gauges: 2½ inches, 3½ inches, 5 inches and 7¼ inches
Web: www.strathavenminiaturerailway.org with information also available on: facebook.com/strathavenminiaturerailway

GENERAL INFORMATION

Nearest Mainline Station: Hamilton (8 miles)
Nearest Bus Station: Hamilton (8 miles)
Car Parking: Available on site
Coach Parking: Available
Souvenir Shop(s): None
Food & Drinks: Available in the Park

SPECIAL INFORMATION

The railway is operated by members of the Strathaven Model Society.

OPERATING INFORMATION

Opening Times: Weekends and Bank Holiday Mondays from Easter until the end of September. Trains run from 1.00pm to 4.30pm.
Steam Working: Most operating days, weather permitting.
Prices: £1.00 per ride

Detailed Directions by Car:
From All Parts: Exit the M74 at Junction 8 and take the A71 through Stonehouse to Strathaven. Turn right onto the A726 and George Allan Park is on the left hand side of the road.

STRAWBERRY LINE MINIATURE RAILWAY

Address: Avon Valley Country Park, Pixash Lane, Keynsham, Bristol BS31 1TP	**N⁰ of Steam Locos**: 5
Telephone N⁰: (0117) 986-4929	**N⁰ of Other Locos**: 30
Year Formed: 1999	**Approx N⁰ of Visitors P.A.**: 100,000
Location: Avon Valley Country Park	**Gauge**: 5 inches
Web site: www.avonvalley.co.uk	**Length of Line**: Two-thirds of a mile
	E-mail: info@avonvalley.co.uk

GENERAL INFORMATION

Nearest Mainline Station: Keynsham (2 miles)
Nearest Bus Station: Bath (6 miles)
Car Parking: Available on site
Coach Parking: Available
Souvenir Shop(s): Yes
Food & Drinks: Available

SPECIAL INFORMATION

The Strawberry Line operates within the Avon Valley Country Park and is the only commercial railway in the UK which uses a 5 inch gauge.

OPERATING INFORMATION

Opening Times: 2019 dates: Daily, except 25th & 26th December and 1st January. Closed on Mondays during local school term times (but open on Bank Holidays). Open from 10.00am to 5.30pm.
Steam Working: Frequently – please contact the railway for further details.
Prices: £2.00 per ride, but see below.
Note: There is a separate admission charge for entry into the Avon Valley Country Park. However, the 'Adventurer Pass' also includes free train rides:
      Adventurer's Pass £15.00
      Toddler Adventurer's Pass £9.00
          (Under-2s and walking babies)
Cheaper rates apply for off-peak visits.

Detailed Directions by Car:
From All Parts: Take the A4 from Bath or Bristol to Keynsham and turn into Pixash Lane following the brown tourist signs for the Country Park.

Summerfields Miniature Railways

Address: Summerfield Barns, High Road, Haynes, Bedford MK45 3BH	**Nº of Steam Locos**: 2 + members locos
Telephone Nº: 07498 869902 (operating days only)	**Nº of Other Locos**: 3 + members locos
	Nº of Members: Approximately 180
Year Formed: 1948	**Annual Membership Fee**: £35.00
Location: Off the A600, North of Haynes	**Approx Nº of Visitors P.A.**: 10,000
Length of Line: Approximately ¾ mile	**Gauge**: 3½ inches, 5 inches & 7¼ inches
	Web site: www.bedfordmes.co.uk

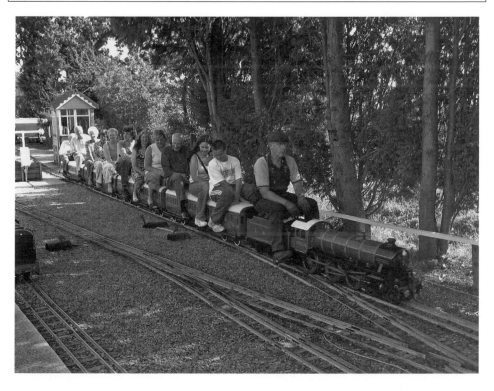

GENERAL INFORMATION

Nearest Mainline Station: Bedford (5½ miles)
Nearest Bus Station: Bedford
Car Parking: Available on site
Coach Parking: Available on site
Souvenir Shop(s): None
Food & Drinks: Available

SPECIAL INFORMATION

Summerfields Miniature Railways is operated by the Bedford Model Engineering Society.

OPERATING INFORMATION

Opening Times: 2019 dates: 10th, 21st & 22nd April; 5th, 6th, 26th, 27th & 29th May; 9th & 23rd June; 7th, 21st, 24th & 31st July; 7th, 14th, 25th & 26th August; 1st & 22nd September; 13th, 23rd & 27th October. Santa Specials run on 7th & 8th December when advance booking is required. Trains run from 10.30am to 3.45pm.
Steam Working: On all public running days
Prices: Adult Return £2.00
Child Return £2.00
Note: Under-5s ride free with a paying adult

Detailed Directions by Car:
From All Parts: The Railway is located by the A600 just to the North of Haynes, 5½ miles South of Bedford and 3½ miles North of Shefford.

SURREY SOCIETY OF MODEL ENGINEERS

Address: Mill Lane, Leatherhead, Surrey, KT22 9AA (No post please as the site does not have a letterbox!)
Telephone Nº: None
Year Formed: 1978
Location of Line: Mill Lane, Leatherhead
Length of Line: 2,000 feet

Nº of Steam Locos: 10
Nº of Other Locos: 8
Nº of Members: 48
Approx Nº of Visitors P.A.: 15,000
Gauge: Both ground and raised level tracks are available covering many gauges
Web site: www.ssme.co.uk
E-mail: enquiries@ssme.co.uk

GENERAL INFORMATION

Nearest Mainline Station: Leatherhead (½ mile)
Nearest Bus Station: Leatherhead (½ mile)
Car Parking: Local town centre car parks only – non available on site
Coach Parking: None
Food & Drinks: Available

OPERATING INFORMATION

Opening Times: 2019 dates: 19th April; 6th & 27th May; 9th June; 26th August; 8th September; 13th October.
Trains run from 11.00am to 4.00pm. Please contact the railway or check their web site for further details.
Steam Working: All operating days.
Prices: £1.80 per ride
£5.00 multi-ride ticket allows 3 rides
£10.00 multi-ride ticket allows 8 rides

Detailed Directions by Car:
The railway is situated near Leatherhead town centre. Mill Lane is across the road from the well signposted Leisure Centre just off the B2122 Waterway Road and just a short walk to the south of Leatherhead Mainline station.

SWANLEY NEW BARN RAILWAY

Address: Swanley Park, New Barn Road, Swanley BR8 7PW	**Nº of Steam Locos**: 7
	Nº of Other Locos: 13
Telephone Nº: None	**Approx Nº of Visitors P.A.**: Not known
Year Formed: 1986	**Gauge**: 7¼ inches
Location of Line: Swanley, Kent	**Web site**: steamdriver.wixsite.com/snbr
Length of Line: 900 yards	

GENERAL INFORMATION

Nearest Mainline Station: Swanley (¾ mile)
Nearest Bus Station: Swanley (¾ mile)
Car Parking: Available on site
Coach Parking: Available
Souvenir Shop(s): None
Food & Drinks: Available in the Park

SPECIAL INFORMATION

The railway is located in a Swanley Park which also has play areas, paddling pool, sandpit, boating lake, cafeteria, bouncy castle and battery bikes all set in 60 acres of parkland with free access and parking.

OPERATING INFORMATION

Opening Times: 2019 dates: Weekends and most days during the School Holidays from 6th April to 27th October. Trains run from 11.00am to 5.00pm.
Steam Working: Regular steam working but on an ad hoc basis.
Prices: Adult Return £1.50
Child Return £1.00 (Ages 3 to 15)
Family Return £4.00 (2 adults + 2 children)
Note: Lower prices apply for single fares and Under-3s ride for free.

Detailed Directions by Car:
From All Parts: Exit the M25 at Junction 3 and follow green signs for Swanley Park. Go straight on at the first roundabout then turn right at the second roundabout. Continue straight on at the next roundabout then turn left at the next crossroads into New Barn Road. The Park is on the left side of the road.

THAMES DITTON MINIATURE RAILWAY

Address: Willowbank, Claygate Lane, Thames Ditton, Surrey   KT7 0LE
Telephone N^o: (020) 8398 3985
Year Formed: 1936
Location of Line: Thames Ditton
Length of Line: ½ mile

N^o of Steam Locos: 30+
N^o of Other Locos: 10+
N^o of Members: Approximately 200
Approx N^o of Visitors P.A.: 15,000
Gauge: 3½ inches, 5 inches & 7¼ inches
Web site: www.malden-dsme.co.uk

GENERAL INFORMATION

Nearest Mainline Station: Thames Ditton (½ mile)
Nearest Bus Station: Thames Ditton
Car Parking: Street parking only
Coach Parking: None
Souvenir Shop(s): Yes
Food & Drinks: Available from 2.30pm onwards

SPECIAL INFORMATION

The railway is operated by Malden and District Society of Model Engineers, is well known locally and is referred to as the Thames Ditton Miniature Railway. The Society operates two tracks at the site – a ground level railway is for larger trains and an elevated railway is for the smaller scale trains. Both are used for passenger hauling services.

OPERATING INFORMATION

Opening Times: Open on Easter Sunday and Monday then the first Sunday of each month and every Bank Holiday Sunday and Monday until the first Sunday in October. Trains run from 2.00pm to 5.30pm though the site is open from 1.00pm onwards. Also open 8th December for pre-booked Santa Specials – please check the web site for further details.
Steam Working: Every operating day.
Prices: Single ride tickets £2.50
Unlimited ride tickets £7.50
Family tickets £27.50

Detailed Directions by Car:
Claygate Lane is located just off the A307 Esher to Kingston road about half a mile to the East of the junction between the A307 and A309. If travelling from the East, Claygate Lane is the turning on the left immediately before the railway bridge. If travelling from the West, Claygate Lane is immediately after the second railway bridge though there is unfortunately, no right turn allowed from this direction.

THORNES PARK MINIATURE RAILWAY

Address: Thornes Park, Lawefield Lane, Wakefield WF2 8QZ	**No of Steam Locos**: 7
Telephone No: (01924) 457690	**No of Other Locos**: 4
Year Formed: 1952	**No of Members**: 40
Location: Thornes Park, Wakefield	**Annual Membership Fee**: £3.00
Length of Line: ½ mile	**Approx No of Visitors P.A.**: 20,000
	Gauges: 7¼ inches

GENERAL INFORMATION

Nearest Mainline Station: Wakefield Westgate (¾ mile)
Nearest Bus Station: Wakefield (1¼ miles)
Car Parking: Available on site
Coach Parking: Available on site
Souvenir Shop(s): None
Food & Drinks: None

SPECIAL INFORMATION

The railway is operated by members of the Wakefield Society of Model and Experimental Engineers. The group is non-profit making and all proceeds after operating costs are donated annually to the Mayor of Wakefield's chosen charity.

OPERATING INFORMATION

Opening Times: Every Sunday (weather permitting) plus Saturdays and Bank Holidays depending on availability of manpower. Trains run from 1.00pm to 5.00pm. Also open for some other special events. Operation is dependent on weather conditions.
Steam Working: Generally whenever the railway is operating.
Prices: Adults 50p
         Children 50p (free of charge for infants)

Detailed Directions by Car:
From All Parts: Thornes Park is located approximately 2 miles from Wakefield City Centre, just off the main Huddersfield to Wakefield road (A638).

Tonbridge Model Engineering Society

Address: The Slade, Castle Grounds, Tonbridge, Kent TN9 1HR	**Nº of Steam Locos:** 40
Telephone Nº: 07776 161811	**Nº of Other Locos:** 10
Year Formed: 1944	**Nº of Members:** Approximately 90
Location: Castle Grounds, Tonbridge	**Approx Nº of Visitors P.A.:** 14,000
Length of Line: ¼ mile	**Gauge:** 3½ inches and 5 inches
	Web site: micklow.wix.com/tmes

GENERAL INFORMATION

Nearest Mainline Station: Tonbridge (1 mile)
Nearest Bus Station: Tonbridge (1 mile)
Car Parking: Available on site
Coach Parking: None
Food & Drinks: Available at the swimming pool cafe.

SPECIAL INFORMATION

The Society has run a track at the present site since 1951 and since then facilities have been extended to include a steaming bay and turntable, passenger trollies, refreshment facilities and meeting room, store, and a well appointed workshop.

OPERATING INFORMATION

Opening Times: 2019 dates: Saturday and Sunday afternoons from 7th April to 27th October, weather permitting. Please contact the railway for further information.
Steam Working: Every operating day.
Prices: Free of charge but donations are accepted.

Detailed Directions by Car:
Exit the A21 Tonbridge Bypass at the junction signposted for Tonbridge South. Drive up the High Street, cross over the River Medway and turn left by the sign for the Swimming Pool. Follow the road round, turn left at Slade School and the car park for the railway is directly ahead.

URMSTON MINIATURE RAILWAY

Address: Urmston & District MES Ltd, Abbotsfield Park, Chassen Road, Flixton, Manchester M41 5DH
Telephone Nº: None
Year Formed: 1948
Location: The Borough of Trafford
Length of Line: 2,200 feet

Nº of Steam Locos: Members' locos only
Nº of Other Locos: Members' locos only
Approx Nº of Visitors P.A.: 5,000+
Gauge: 3½ inches and 5 inches
Web site: www.udmes.co.uk

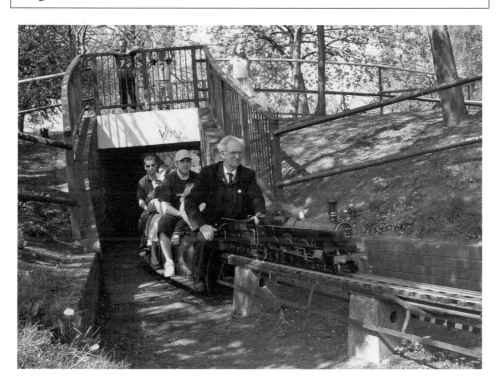

GENERAL INFORMATION

Nearest Mainline Station: Urmston (1 mile) (Chassen Road Station is closer but no trains stop there on Sundays!)
Nearest Bus Station: Central Manchester (7 miles)
Car Parking: Street parking only
Coach Parking: None
Souvenir Shop(s): None
Food & Drinks: Available from an ice cream van

OPERATING INFORMATION

Opening Times: Sundays throughout the year, except for Christmas Day. Open from approximately 11.00pm to 3.30pm.
Steam Working: Please contact the Society for further information.
Prices: 30p per ride

Detailed Directions by Car:
From the North: Exit the M60 at Junction 10 and take the 3rd exit onto the B2514 heading southwards. Continue straight on at two roundabouts passing the Nag's Head pub into Crofts Bank Road. Shortly after passing the Sainsbury's store, turn right into Flixton Road and pass Urmston station. Continue along Flixton Road then turn left at the roundabout into Chassen Road for the Abbotsfield Park; From the South: Exit the M60 at Junction 9 and turn left onto the B5158 Lostock Road. After approximately ¾ mile, turn left at the roundabout onto Crofts Bank Road (the B2514). Then as above.

VOGRIE PARK MINIATURE RAILWAY

Contact Address: Eskvalley MES,
Roslin Glen Country Park, Roslin,
Midlothian EH25 9PX
Phone Nº: 07754 441211 (Secretary)
Year Formed: 1982
Location of Line: Vogrie Country Park
Length of Line: 2200 feet

Nº of Steam Locos: 3 (Member's locos)
Nº of Other Locos: 5
Nº of Members: 30
Approx Nº of Visitors P.A.: 6,000
Gauge: 5 inches and 7¼ inches
Web site: www.eskvalleymes.org.uk
E-mail: info@eskvalleymes.org.uk

GENERAL INFORMATION

Nearest Mainline Station: Gorebridge (6.5 miles)
Nearest Bus Station: Cranston
Car Parking: Available on site
Coach Parking: Available on site
Food & Drinks: Available on site

SPECIAL INFORMATION

The Eskvalley MES operates a railway in the grounds
of the Vogrie Country Park which comprises 105
hectares of woods and Victorian parkland including
a 1876 Victorian mansion (part of which is open to
the public), a nine-hole golf course, adventure
playground and a cafeteria.

OPERATING INFORMATION

Opening Times: Sundays from Easter to September.
Trains run from 1.00pm to 5.00pm.
Steam Working: As available.
Prices: £1.00 per person per ride.
Party bookings can be arranged on other days.
Please phone Bill on 07484 324614 for further
information.

Detailed Directions by Car:
From Dalkeith: Travel South on the A68 for 2½ miles then turn right onto the B6372 signposted for Vogrie
Country Park. Continue along this road for the Park; From the A7: Travel towards Gorebridge and turn off onto
the B6372. Pass through Gorebridge staying on the B6372, continue through Newlandrig for the Park.

WELLING AND DISTRICT M.E.S.

Address: Falconwood Depot, Eltham Grid Station, off Rochester Way, London, SE9 2RE
Telephone Nº: None
Year Formed: 1945
Location of Line: Adjacent to the UK Power Networks Site, just off Rochester Way
Length of Line: 2000 feet

Nº of Steam Locos: Member's locos only
Nº of Other Locos: Member's locos only
Approx Nº of Visitors P.A.: Not known
Gauge: 3½ inches & 5 inches (raised track)
Web site: www.wdmes.co.uk

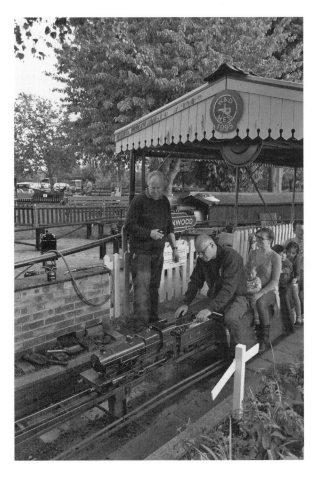

GENERAL INFORMATION

Nearest Mainline Station:
Falconwood (¼ mile)
Car Parking: Adjacent to the site. Blue Disabled badge holders only can park on the site.
Souvenir Shop: None
Food & Drinks: Hot and cold drinks plus snacks are available

SPECIAL INFORMATION

The railway operates on a site which is owned by UK Power Networks.

OPERATING INFO

Opening Times: 2019 dates:
7th & 21st April; 5th & 19th May;
2nd, 16th & 30th June;
14th & 28th July; 11th & 25th August;
8th & 22nd September; 6th October
(last running date).
Trains run from 2.00pm to 5.00pm.
Note: Due to the National Grid building a new cable tunnel from Bexley to Woolwich, the railway is being forced to relocate from Falconwood following the public running days in 2019. At the time of going to print, no new site had been found so please check the Society's web site for further details of operations in future years.
Steam Working: All operating days.
Prices: 60p per ride.

Detailed Directions by Car:
The railway is located on the old National Grid site, just off Rochester Way, close to the A2 and near to Falconwood Station. Rochester Way can be accessed directly from the A2 westbound at the Falconwood turn-off. Alternatively, turn off the South Circular at Well Hall Roundabout into Rochester Way, and the railway is then 1¼ miles.

WEST HUNTSPILL M.E.S.

Correspondence: 10 Beal Way,
Burnham-on-Sea   TA8 1JS
Telephone Nº: 07766228676
Year Formed: The club was formed in the
1950s, the track was established in 1967
Length of Line: 1,062 feet (raised) and
827 feet (ground level) when complete.
Gauge: 3½ inches & 5 inches (raised track)

Location: West Huntspill Memorial
Playing Fields, New Road, West Huntspill,
TA9 3QE
Nº of Steam Locos: Members' locos only
Nº of Other Locos: Members' locos only
Nº of Members: 65
Approx Nº of Visitors P.A.: 8,000
Web site: www.westhuntspillmes.co.uk
also   www.facebook.com/huntspill

GENERAL INFORMATION

Nearest Mainline Station:
Highbridge (1¼ miles)
Nearest Bus Station:
Highbridge (1 mile)
Car Parking: Onsite parking available
in dry weather, otherwise roadside
parking only.
Souvenir Shop(s): None
Food & Drinks: Available

SPECIAL INFORMATION

Although the West Huntspill Model
Engineering Society was first formed in
the early 1950s, the present site was first
used in 1967.

OPERATING INFO

Opening Times: 2019 dates: Every
Sunday from Easter to the end of
October, from 2.00pm to 4.30pm,
depending on the weather. Please check
facebook for information about Special
Events such as Santa Specials in
December.
Steam Working: Most operating days,
but dependent on which members bring
in their locos.
Prices: £1.00 per ride (2 laps)
£5.00 for 6 rides

Detailed Directions by Car:
The society's track is located on the West Huntspill Memorial Playing Field. Take the A38 and turn into New Road
by West Huntspill School and the playing fields are on the left after ¼ mile.

WESTON PARK RAILWAY

Address: Weston Park, Weston-under-Lizard, Shifnal, Shropshire TF11 8LE
Telephone Nº: 07952 850336 (Railway) or (01952) 852100 (Weston Park)
Year Formed: 1980
Location of Line: Weston Park
Length of Line: Approximately 1¼ miles

Nº of Steam Locos: Variable
Nº of Other Locos: Variable
Approx Nº of Visitors P.A.: 19,500
Gauge: 7¼ inches
Web site: www.weston-park.com
E-mail: bruce@westonrail.co.uk

GENERAL INFORMATION

Nearest Mainline Station: Shifnal (6 miles)
Nearest Bus Station: –
Car Parking: Available on site
Coach Parking: Available on site
Souvenir Shop(s): –
Food & Drinks: Available

SPECIAL INFORMATION

The railway operates in the grounds of Weston Park (www.weston-park.com), a stately home with a large park and gardens designed by 'Capability' Brown. Weston Park also has a number of other attractions for all the family.

OPERATING INFORMATION

Opening Times: 2019 dates: Daily from 13th April to 28th April, weekends in May then daily from 24th May to 1st September. Trains run from 11.30am.
Steam Working: Please contact the railway for further details: info@westonrail.co.uk
Prices: Adults £2.50
  Children £2.50 (Under-2s ride for free)
Note: Prices shown above are for train fares only. An admission charge is made for entry into the park, gardens and stately home. This admission fee is required for use of the railway. Please contact Weston Park for admission price information.

Detailed Directions by Car:
From All Parts: Weston Park is situated by the side of the A5 in Weston-under-Lizard, Shropshire, just 3 miles from the M54 (exit at Junction 3 and take the A41 northwards) and 8 miles West of the M6 (exit at Junction 12).

WILLEN MINIATURE RAILWAY

Address: South Willen Lake, Milton Keynes MK15 0DS **Telephone Nº:** 07810 131737 **Year Formed:** 1989 **Location of Line:** Milton Keynes **Length of Line:** 600 yards	**Nº of Steam Locos:** None **Nº of Other Locos:** 1 **Approx Nº of Visitors P.A.:** More than one million visitors to the Park each year **Gauge:** 7¼ inches **Web site:** www.willenlake.org.uk

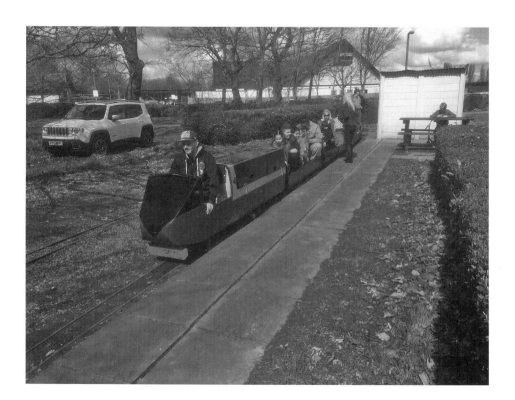

GENERAL INFORMATION

Nearest Mainline Station: Milton Keynes Central (1½ miles)
Nearest Bus Station: Milton Keynes (1½ miles)
Car Parking: Available on site
Coach Parking: Available
Souvenir Shop(s): None
Food & Drinks: Available

OPERATING INFORMATION

Opening Times: Weekends and daily during the summer School Holidays from Easter until the end of October. Open from 11.00am to 6.00pm.
Steam Working: None
Prices: £2.00 per ride

Detailed Directions by Car:
From All Parts: Exit the M1 at Junction 14 and follow the H6 towards Milton Keynes. The lake is to the left of the road by the V10 (Brickhill Street).

WOKING MINIATURE RAILWAY (MIZENS)

Address: Barrs Lane, Knaphill, Woking, Surrey GU21 2JW	**Nº of Steam Locos:** 10
Telephone Nº: (020) 8890-1978	**Nº of Other Locos:** 16
E-mail: mizensrailway@rjjagriff.me	**Nº of Members:** 100
Year Formed: 1989	**Annual Membership Fee:** £15.00
Location of Line: Knaphill, Surrey	**Approx Nº of Visitors P.A.:** 20,000
Length of Line: 1 mile	**Gauge:** 7¼ inches
	Web site: www.mizensrailway.co.uk

GENERAL INFORMATION

Nearest Mainline Station: Woking (2½ miles)
Nearest Bus Station: Woking
Car Parking: 175 spaces available on site
Coach Parking: Available on site but advance notification of the visit is necessary.
Souvenir Shop(s): Yes
Food & Drinks: Tea shop open on running days

SPECIAL INFORMATION

The Railway, which celebrates 30 years of operation in 2019, is situated in a beautiful location amidst 9 acres of woodland and takes its name from Mizens Farm which was its original location but is now the headquarters of the McLaren F1 team!

OPERATING INFORMATION

Opening Times: 2019 dates: Easter Sunday then every Sunday from 5th May to 29th September. Also open on Thursdays in August and Santa Specials run on 8th, 15th & 22nd December.
Please check the web site for further details.
Trains operate from 2.00pm to 5.00pm.
Steam Working: Most operating days
Prices: Adult Return From £2.00 or £2.50
 Child Return From £2.00 or £2.50
Note: Prices vary depending on the route and Santa Specials must be pre-booked.

Detailed Directions by Car:
From All Parts: Exit the M25 at Junction 11 and follow the A320 to Woking. At the Six Cross Roads Roundabout take the 5th exit towards Knaphill then turn left at the roundabout onto Littlewick Road. Continue along Littlewick Road crossing the roundabout before turning right into Barrs Lane just before Knaphill.

WOLDS WAY LAVENDER

Address: Wintringham, Malton, North Yorkshire YO17 8HW	**Nº of Steam Locos**: None
Telephone Nº: (01944) 758641	**Nº of Other Locos**: 1
Year Formed: 2004	**Approx Nº of Visitors P.A.**: 30,000
Location of Line: Malton, N. Yorkshire	**Gauge**: 7¼ inches
Length of Line: 200 metres	**Web site**: www.woldswaylavender.co.uk
	E-mail: admin@woldswaylavender.co.uk

GENERAL INFORMATION

Nearest Mainline Station: Malton (6 miles)
Nearest Bus Station: Yorkshire Coastliner Bus Service runs between Leeds, Tadcaster, Malton & Scarborough. (Tel 01653 692556). Unfortunately, there is a half a mile walk from the bus stop.
Car Parking: Free parking available on site
Coach Parking: Free parking available on site
Souvenir Shop(s): Yes
Food & Drinks: Available

SPECIAL INFORMATION

Wolds Way Lavender operates one of the few working miniature railways in the country. The train is used to bring the Lavender in from the fields to the Distillery. The train also carries the logs to fire the still in addition to the passenger carriages that are used for train rides.

OPERATING INFORMATION

Opening Times: 2019 dates: Daily from Saturday 30th March until Sunday 29th September. Trains Open from 10.00am to 4.00pm (but until 5.00pm in July and August).
Steam Working: None at present
Prices: £2.00 per ride.
Note: Admission is charged for entry to Lavender Fields which is required to access rides:
      Adults £6.00   Concessions £5.50
      Children £5.00 (Under-2s admitted free)
      Family Tickets £20.00 and £22.00

Detailed Directions by Car:
Wolds Way Lavender is half a mile off the A64 York to Scarborough road on the Scarborough side of Malton. Look out for the Brown tourist signs for Wolds Way Lavender on the main road.

WOLVERHAMPTON & DISTRICT M.E.S.

Address: Baggeridge Country Park, Near Sedgley, Staffordshire DY3 4HB	**Nº of Steam Locos**: 15
Telephone Nº: (01922) 476373	**Nº of Other Locos**: 7
Year Formed: 1986	**Nº of Members**: 60
Location: Baggeridge Country Park	**Approx Nº of Visitors P.A.**: Not known
Length: Ground level line is being extended to 2,100 feet. Raised track is 420 feet	**Gauge**: 3½ inches, 5 inches & 7¼ inches
	Website: www.wolverhampton-dmes.co.uk

GENERAL INFORMATION

Nearest Mainline Station: Wolverhampton (7 miles)
Nearest Bus Station: Sedgley (2 miles)
Car Parking: Available on site
Coach Parking: Available on site
Food & Drinks: Available

SPECIAL INFORMATION

The Wolverhampton & District Model Engineering Society operates the railway which runs through the Baggeridge Country Park. This was formerly the Baggeridge Colliery and part of the original Himley Estate of the Earls of Dudley. Since the closure of the Colliery, the site has been transformed into 150 acres of attractive country park.

OPERATING INFORMATION

Opening Times: 2019 dates: Public running commences on Easter Sunday, then on all Bank Holidays and most Sundays until mid-September. Detailed information is available on the web site. The railway also operates on Tuesdays and Thursdays during the School Holidays when staff are available. Trains run from 1.00pm to 5.00pm, weather permitting.
Steam Working: Most operating days.
Prices: No charge but donations are accepted.

Detailed Directions by Car:
Take the A449 Wolverhampton to Kidderminster road then turn onto the A463 towards Sedgley. Baggeridge Country Park is just to the South of the A463 after approximately 1 mile and is well-signposted from the road.

WOODSEAVES MINIATURE RAILWAY

Address: Woodseaves Garden Plants,
Sydnall Lane Nursery, Woodseaves,
Market Drayton   TF9 2AS
Telephone Nº: (01630) 653161
Year Formed: 2004
Location of Line: Shropshire
Length of Line: Over 400 yards

Nº of Steam Locos: 2
Nº of Other Locos: 2
Approx Nº of Visitors P.A.: 1,500
Gauge: 7¼ inches
Web site: www.woodseavesminirail.co.uk
Facebook: Woodseaves Miniature Railway

GENERAL INFORMATION

Nearest Mainline Station: Shrewsbury (19 miles)
Nearest Bus Station: Market Drayton (3 miles)
Car Parking: Available on site
Coach Parking: A small amount of space available
Souvenir Shop(s): None
Food & Drinks: Available in the Tea Shed

SPECIAL INFORMATION

There are two 'Woodseaves' garden centres in close proximity! Specialist Plant Nursery and Gardens Groups are welcome by prior arrangement.

OPERATING INFORMATION

Opening Times: 2019 dates: Sundays and Bank Holidays from Easter to September during afternoons. Please contact the railway for further details.
Steam Working: Most operating days
Prices: £2.00
Note: Children must be accompanied by an adult and Under-2s ride for free.

Detailed Directions by Car:
From All Parts: The railway is located just off the A529 at Woodseaves, Shropshire which is situated approximately 2 miles to the south of Market Drayton.